# HERBAGE INTAKE HANDBOOK

# HERBAGE INTAKE HANDBOOK

## SECOND EDITION

Edited by:

**P.D. PENNING**

Published by:

**The British Grassland Society**

First published 1982
This edition 2004

ISBN 0 905944 31 3

The authors or their informants have had direct experience of the items of
equipment and proprietary products identified by name. However, the
comments made in this book are not intended to be exhaustive and no exclusive
endorsement of named products is implied.

# CONTENTS

# LIST OF CONTRIBUTORS

R.D. BAKER, BSc, MSc, CDFM, Formerly Head of the Cattle and Sheep Production Department, Institute of Grassland and Environmental Research, Hurley and Shinfield Research Stations.

R. BAUMONT, Ingénieur Agronome, Docteur de l'Institut National Agronomique, Head of the Animal-Plant Relationship Research Group, Herbivore Research Unit, Institut National de la Recherche Agronomique, Clermont-Ferrand/Theix, France.

M. CHENOST, Ingénieur Agronome, Former member of the Feed Laboratory, Herbivore Nutrition Research Station, Institut National de la Recherche Agronomique, Clermont-Ferrand/Theix, France.

C. DEMARQUILLY, Ingénieur Agronome, Formerly Head of the Feed Laboratory, Herbivore Nutrition Research Station, Institut National de la Recherche Agronomique, Clermont-Ferrand/Theix, France.

J. HODGSON, BSc, PhD, DSc, FRSNZ, CPAg. Emeritus Professor of Pastoral Science, Institute of Natural Resources, Massey University, Palmerston North, New Zealand.

E.A. LANTINGA, BSc, MSc, PhD, Associate Professor, Group of Biological Farming Systems, Wageningen University, The Netherlands.

J.A.C. MEIJS, BSc, MSc, PhD, Head of the Innovation Centre Organic Agriculture, Wageningen University and Research Centre, Wageningen, The Netherlands.

J.H. NEUTEBOOM, BSc, MSc, Former Staff Member of the Department of Plant Sciences, Wageningen University, The Netherlands.

P.D. PENNING, CBiol, MIBiol, Research Associate, Institute of Grassland and Environmental Research, North Wyke, Okehampton, Devon EX20 2SB UK.

A.J. ROOK, BSc, PhD, Team Leader, Behavioural and Community Ecology, Institute of Grassland and Environmental Research, North Wyke, Okehampton, Devon EX20 2SB UK.

S.M. RUTTER, BSc, MSc., PhD, Member of the Institute of Grassland and Environmental Research, North Wyke, Okehampton, Devon EX20 2SB UK.

R.J. WILKINS, BSc, PhD, DSc, FIBiol, F.R.Ag.S., Visiting Professor Universities of Reading and Plymouth, Past President BGS. Research Associate, Institute of Grassland and Environmental Research, North Wyke, Okehampton, Devon EX20 2SB UK.

# PREFACE

The objective of the Second Edition of The Herbage Intake Handbook is to describe methods of measuring herbage intake by grazing animals and is a companion to the Sward Measurement Hanbook edited by Alison Davies, R.D. Baker, Sheila Grant and A.S. Laidlaw published by the British Grassland Society in 1993. It updates the 1st edition published in 1982.

The authors of this Handbook are experts in their own fields who have been involved in grazing studies for many years. The views expressed here are those of the authors and the reviews and details of techniques given are not necessarily exhaustive. Also, the use of commercial names applied to equipment does not necessarily imply endorsement of the products or suggest that alternatives are not available.

I am extremely grateful to the authors of chapters for the way they have dealt with such difficult subjects and to Professor Wilkins for writing the foreword.

Finally, I should like to thank my wife and I promise that I will now do some decorating!


March 2004

P.D.Penning, North Wyke

# FOREWORD

Grazing is the predominant method for harvesting and utilising grassland on a global basis. The grazed herbage is a major feed resource for ruminant animals and grazing has profound effects on the composition and structure of grasslands and rangelands. The quantity of feed consumed is probably the most important single factor determining the rate of animal production and feed conversion efficiency by ruminants. It is relatively easy to determine feed intake by housed animals, as weighed quantities of feeds can be given to the animals and uneaten feed can be collected and weighed. This approach cannot be followed with grazing animals, which consume herbage from a growing sward in the field. The problem of measuring herbage intake by grazing animals has been addressed by researchers over many years. Widely contrasting approaches have been followed, with the focus for measurement being on changes in the sward, on the ingestive activity of the grazing animal or on a calculation of the nutrients required to support the measured level of animal performance.

The British Grassland Society took the initiative to commission and publish the first edition of the Herbage Intake Handbook in 1982. In view of the continued importance of herbage intake and innovations that have been made in techniques, the Society commissioned this second edition and Peter Penning, a Research Associate of the Institute of Grassland and Environmental Research, agreed to be editor. He has been responsible for many technical innovations and has a wealth of experience in grazing, having carried out a vast number of experiments in contrasting situations during a distinguished career. In addition to editing the book, he is senior author of two chapters and brought together an international group of expert authors. The contribution of authors from France, the Netherlands and New Zealand ensures a wide perspective.

The chapters on 'Sward methods' and 'Estimating herbage intake from animal performance' have altered relatively little from the first edition, reflecting the relative maturity of these areas. Progress with improved sensors, methods of data capture and analysis and new developments in analytical chemistry have had profound effects on the approaches that can be used in assessing intake by animal-based techniques and this is reflected in the major changes in the chapters dealing with these aspects.

The authors repeatedly stress that there is no single best method for measuring herbage intake. Researchers must be clear as to why an assessment of intake is required in relation to the objectives of their particular experiment. They must then identify an appropriate technique in relation to their reasons for assessing intake, the precision required and the facilities available. The resources required vary immensely between the different techniques. Methods based on animal performance and some of the sward methods, may require very few measurements in addition to those already being made for other purposes. With many of the other animal-based methods, on the other hand, there will be need for substantial investment in equipment and expertise and a high labour input, but generally the resulting estimates of intake will be more robust and ancillary information will also be obtained. One of the most important contributions of this book is to provide guidelines on the strengths and weaknesses and areas of applicability of the techniques described in the various chapters. The inclusion in this edition of a chapter on 'Statistical considerations in the design of herbage intake studies' is particularly valuable. There are hazards in this area and it is self evident that effort in measuring herbage intake is wasted, if the basic experimental design is flawed.

I am convinced that this book will make a major contribution to further increase the efficiency of grazing research, giving, in the long run, benefits for both production efficiency and the environment.

January 2004

R.J. Wilkins, *North Wyke*

CHAPTER 1

# MEASUREMENTS OF HERBAGE INTAKE AND INGESTIVE BEHAVIOUR IN GRAZING ANIMALS: AN INTRODUCTION

**J. Hodgson**

*"...it continues to fascinate me that we have developed such precise methods of estimating the intake of grazing animals. Even the so called direct methods are an achievement and the indirect methods seem little short of miraculous." (Holmes, 1982).*

## 1.1 BACKGROUND

In his introductory chapter to the first edition of this Handbook, Greenhalgh (1982) emphasised the importance of a realistic assessment of the random errors and consistent biases involved in the alternative procedures for estimating the herbage intake of grazing animals. He drew attention to the complexity of some of the methods available, and the need therefore to justify the measurement of herbage intake and diet composition in any particular research project. He described this approach to herbage intake measurement as "cautious, critical and even pessimistic", but suggested that "the reader should not allow caution to totally repress enthusiasm."

The tone of these comments might be considered to be unduly pessimistic, with the emphasis more on risk than on information gain, but it is justified in terms of a deliberate attempt to encourage the reader to be critical and objective in deciding on the priorities for evaluating resource allocation in grazing experiments - this argument, of course, applying to the full range of measurements of animal, vegetation, soil and environmental variables which would be possible, and may be desirable, in any grazing study. Similar views are expressed by Coates and Penning (2000) in the latest edition of another recent book on field and laboratory techniques in grassland research (Mannetje and Jones, 2000).

Greenhalgh (1982) commented on the laborious nature of procedures for estimating forage intake, and suggested that these procedures should not be attempted "unless (a) a definite requirement for them can be established, and (b) they can be made with a degree of accuracy appropriate to the needs of the experiment." One of the more valuable functions in the chapters which follow is to provide examples of the variability and/or bias expected for particular techniques, and the appropriate practical and statistical procedures for dealing with these sources of variation. Greenhalgh (1982) suggested that a measure of the need for intake measurement might be evidence for, or expectation of, differences in animal performance resulting from the treatments prescribed. This might now be considered to be a rather narrow prescription of need or opportunity, because circumstances can readily be imagined where differences in the quantity and nutritive value of the herbage eaten are self-cancelling in their effects on animal performance in the short term, but may have very different implications to the overall productivity and sustainability of the treatments compared. In a more general sense, measurements of herbage consumption and diet selection would be seen as major components of many ecosystem studies, irrespective of expectation of effects on individual animal performance.

## 1.2 TECHNIQUE DEVELOPMENTS

It is instructive to ask the question "What changes have taken place in the 20 years since the publication of the original edition of this Handbook (Leaver, 1982) which affect the choice of procedures for measuring herbage intake and diet composition?" Four main factors seem to be of importance:

a.  Development of instrumentation for the automatic recording of aspects of grazing behaviour in free-grazing animals (Penning and Rutter, 2004), facilitating the adoption of advances in the flexibility, continuity and detail of data collection and processing procedures.

b.  Rapid development of technology to make use of an increasing range of plant micro-constituents (most notably the cuticular waxes and associated lipids (Dove and Mayes, 1991), for use as quantitative markers in measurements of both herbage intake and diet composition. This development has not changed the basic parameters which determine the choice of what to measure, and how to make measurements, but it has allowed much greater flexibility of choice in managing and monitoring animals in grazing studies.

c.  The increasing restriction on the use of surgically prepared animals resulting from the development and application of animal welfare regulations, particularly in the context of grazing experiments where public access is difficult to control. This is not in any sense to question the ethical issues involved, but welfare controls have impacted particularly on techniques for the determination of diet composition, where procedures based on the use of animals fistulated at the oesophagus had come to be widely used.

d.  Progressive recognition of the commonality of interest between natural ecologists and agricultural ecologists in measurements of diet quantity and composition as important elements in understanding the outcomes of ecosystem research. This has tended to increase demands on the flexibility, as well as the reliability of intake measurements, because it has involved increasing interest in relatively broad-based ecosystem studies.

Superficially, concerns about the reliability and flexibility of procedures for estimating herbage intake and diet composition may seem to be much the same as they were 20 years ago. However, closer examination of published papers suggests that there has been substantial increase in the complexity of grazing experiments over this time, reflecting the greater flexibility of measurement techniques and the greater efficiency of data capture made possible by new analytical procedures and more sophisticated monitoring and data processing equipment. This has meant something of a change in emphasis from relatively simple experimental designs involving contrasts in plant species or cultivars, herbage allowance or stocking rate, often under closely controlled rotational managements, to relatively complex comparisons of alternative plant communities or management strategies, often in quite large-scale studies with minimum pasture control.

It is a moot point as to whether research demands have driven technique development, or technique innovation and development have encouraged more ambitious studies. It is clear, however, that there is still scope for initiative in this area of methodology, and a genuine need for techniques which span a range of spatial and time scales in order to facilitate the coordination of data bases which are currently subject, to a greater or lesser extent, to cross-scale limitations.

## 1.3 MEASUREMENT TECHNIQUES

The focus in this Handbook is on the measurement, or the prediction, of herbage intake and diet composition in grazing animals. Thus measurements made on housed animals, though clearly of value in their own right, are considered in Chapter 5 (Baumont *et al.*, 2004) in the context of their potential for predicting intake under grazing conditions. Bearing this emphasis in mind, the measurement techniques described in the Handbook are grouped into five main categories:

a. Measurements of forage intake by housed animals fed on fresh or conserved herbage (Chapter 5: Baumont *et al.*, 2004. These procedures provide the closest control of both random error and bias in intake measurement, and clear definition of variation between individual animals. They are particularly appropriate to studies on ruminant nutrition, but cannot be expected to account for the range of sward structural variables which influence the selective behaviour and herbage intake of free-grazing animals (Baumont *et al.*, 2004).

b. Techniques based on the calculation of nutrient (usually energy) requirements of grazing animals predicted from feeding standards (Chapter 4: Baker 2004). In these procedures control of random error and bias is heavily dependent upon careful control of relatively routine measurements of animal body weight and production of milk or wool. They are probably best used in comparisons of farm-scale production or the performance of relatively large groups of experimental animals. Calculations of nutrient requirements can provide a cross-check on the accuracy of alternative procedures, but this in itself involves some assumptions about the validity of feeding standards for field conditions.

c.  Sward measurement procedures, in which estimates of herbage intake and diet composition are derived from the difference between measurements made before and after grazing (Chapter 2: Lantinga *et al.,* 2004).

These procedures can provide the opportunity for good control of random variation, but are less effective in controlling bias. They are particularly useful when applied to closely controlled rotational management practices, but are usually used in circumstances which limit measurements of herbage intake to means (or totals) for groups of animals.

d.  Estimates of herbage intake and diet composition in free-grazing animals, mainly using marker techniques based on natural plant constituents or introduced markers (Chapter 3: Penning, 2004). These procedures can provide estimates of forage intake and diet composition across a wide range of pasture conditions and grazing managements, with minimal requirements for grazing control. With current methodology prediction of results for individual animals is possible, but the techniques are subject to both random error and bias, and should not be used without the adoption of appropriate "check" procedures to monitor both sources of variation.

e.  Observations on the components of foraging strategy and ingestive behaviour in grazing animals (Chapter 6: Penning and Rutter, 2004). These measurements are of interest in their own right, but can also be used, in combination, to calculate herbage intake. They are also prone to both random error and bias, which should be checked wherever possible.

The distinctions drawn between these five sets of procedures are somewhat artificial. For example, it is feasible to make estimates of herbage intake from pre- and post-grazing sward measurements on areas grazed by individually tethered animals and at the same time to monitor grazing behaviour (e.g. Doughty *et al.,* 1992).

In general, however, developing interest in the measurement of herbage intake in ecosystem studies, together with improvements in the flexibility and reliability of animal-based measurements, has meant that procedures described in Chapters 3 and 6 have become progressively favoured in grazing research. It is appropriate, therefore, that Chapter 7 (Rook, 2004) should deal primarily with statistical considerations in the design of and analysis of results from experiments based on this technology.

The increasing capacity to monitor herbage intake and grazing behaviour in large-scale studies (paddock, field, range) and relatively complex environments has been paralleled by equally valuable improvements in the methodology of small-scale studies (mini-sward, sward board) on the mechanisms of the grazing process. These latter developments have allowed greater precision in describing the components of grazing behaviour and defining the mechanics of the grazing process (Chapter 5; Baumont *et al.,* 2004), but reservations have been expressed about these procedures in terms of their limited relevance to ecosystem-scale application (e.g. Taylor, 1993). This conflict of interest between experimental control and scale of application can of course be generalised to most biological questions, but it continues to be of particular concern in grazing studies. In this context, it is encouraging to note that there is a substantial degree of commonality in the development of understanding of both animal and plant behaviour at a range of spatial scales (Hodgson and Da Silva, 2000 ).

Many authors have emphasised the need to distinguish between the components of variance in estimates of intake or diet composition which reflect random errors in measurement procedures, and those due to genuine between-animal differences in behaviour (e.g. Greenhalgh, 1982). It can be quite difficult to separate out these sources of variation without the use of repetitive designs, including change-over designs (Bransby and Maclaurin, 2000) which may themselves compromise the continuity of measurement of some system effects. The use of group mean values in replicated studies, rather than values for individual animals may help to constrain some risks of invalid interpretation of data (Rook, 2004), but this needs to be balanced against the potential value of information on individual animal variation for extrapolation to population studies and within-group interactions.

## 1.4 THE PLACE OF INTAKE MEASUREMENTS IN GRAZING STUDIES

Most procedures for monitoring herbage intake and diet composition are demanding in resources and management, so it is important to maximise their value in a research programme. Greenhalgh (1982) focused primarily on the use of intake information to explain observed variations in animal performance, but it is also true that the value of intake studies can be greatly enhanced by associated measurements on vegetation characteristics and management factors which themselves influence foraging behaviour and nutrient intake. In particular, detailed information on the spatial distribution of plant components may well be necessary in order to understand observations on diet composition and forage intake, with information on foraging strategy and ingestive behaviour forming the link between them (Hodgson, 1981). Recognition of the importance of vegetation heterogeneity, and procedures to describe it, is also important (Laca and Lemaire, 2000).

These considerations dictate the importance of a thorough evaluation of the desirability and availability of techniques for measuring "explanatory variables" in intake studies. Such deliberations need to take into account both the labour and equipment demands of alternative techniques, and the risks of interference with the management objectives of a particular experiment. This is one of the main reasons why observations on herbage intake are usually made at intervals rather than on a continuous basis.

The high resource demands of many procedures for measuring forage intake and diet composition, or vegetation composition and structure, emphasise the importance of effective pooling of resources in grazing trials in order to maximise the capture of component information in coordinated, inter-disciplinary studies. This may appear to be self-evident logic, but modern research funding strategies do little to encourage studies of this kind, and it is increasingly unusual to see examples of studies where there is thorough monitoring of animal, plant and soil variables and where a quantitative description of tissue flows through the plant and animal components is possible. With these issues in mind, the reader would be well advised to consult the Companion Sward Measurement Handbook (Davies *et al.,* 1993) and the more broadly based Field and Laboratory methods for Grassland and Animal Production Research (Mannetje and Jones, 2000) for critical coverage of sward as well as animal measurement techniques.

The risk implicit in any grazing study which is heavily loaded with experimental measurements is that the design and management of the experiment will be chosen for their convenience to measurement routines. The opposite should always be the case, with measurement procedures chosen to suit the management objectives.

## 1.5 CONCLUSIONS

Technique bulletins like this often seem to be written by experienced people for experienced people, but a book of this size cannot hope to cover all the nuances of the many techniques described in outline. It is important that scientists contemplating new areas of research or new measurement techniques should talk to and, if possible, work with experienced practitioners before making up their minds about new procedures. But experience is only part of the picture. There is still need, and opportunity, for new initiatives to improve the accuracy and flexibility of techniques for measuring herbage intake and diet composition. Greenhalgh (1982) concluded his introductory chapter to the original Handbook with the comment "There is a great deal to be learned about the intake of grazing animals and there is plenty of scope for improving the methodology of intake measurement." The comment is as appropriate now as it was 20 years ago.

## 1.6 REFERENCES

BAKER R.D. (2004). Estimating herbage intake from animal performance. In P.D. Penning (ed). *Herbage Intake Handbook*. 2nd edn. The British Grassland Society. pp. 95-120.

BAUMONT R., CHENOST M. and DEMARQUILLY C. (2004). Measurement of herbage intake and ingestive behaviour by housed animals. In: Penning P.D. (ed). *Herbage Intake Handbook*. 2nd edn. The British Grassland Society pp. 121-150.

BRANSBY D.I. and MACLAURIN A.R. (2000). Designing animal production studies. In: L. t'Mannetje L. and Jones R.M.(eds). *Field and Laboratory Methods for Grassland and Animal Production Research*. CABI Publishing, Wallingford, Oxon. pp. 327-352.

COATES D.B. and PENNING P.D. (2000). Measuring animal performance. In: t'Mannetje L. and Jones R.M. (eds). *Field and Laboratory Methods for Grassland and Animal Production Research*. CABI Publishing, Wallingford, Oxon. pp. 353-402.

DAVIES Alison, BAKER R.D., GRANT Sheila A. and LAIDLAW A.S. (1993), Sward Measurement Handbook. British Grassland Society. 319pp.

DOUGHERTY C.T., BRADLEY M.W., LAURIAULT L.M., ARIAS J.E., and CORNELIUS P.L. (1992). Allowance-intake relations of cattle grazing vegetative tall fescue. *Grass and Forage Science*, **47**, 211-219.

DOVE H. and MAYES R.W. (1991). The use of plant alkanes as marker substances in studies of the nutrition of herbivores: a review. *Australian Journal of Agricultural Research*, **42**, 913-952.

GREENHALGH J.F.D. (1982). An introduction to herbage intake measurements. In: Leaver J.D. (ed). *Herbage Intake Handbook*. 1st edn. The British Grassland Society, pp 1-10.

HODGSON J. (1981). Sward studies: objectives and priorities. In: Hodgson J., Baker R.D., Davies A., Laidlaw A.S. and Leaver J.D.(eds) *Sward Measurement Handbook*. 1st edn. British Grassland Society, pp.1-14.

HODGSON J. and DA SILVA S.C. (2000). Sustainability of grazing systems: goals, concepts and methods. In: Lemaire G., Hodgson J., de Moraes A., Nabinger C.and de F. Carvalho P.D. (eds). *Grassland Ecophysiology and Grazing Ecology.* CABI Publishing, Wallingford, Oxon. pp. 1-13.

HOLMES W. (1982). Foreword. In: Leaver J.D. (ed). *Herbage Intake Handbook*. 1st edn. British Grassland Society, p.vi.

LACA E.A. and LEMAIRE G. (2000). Measuring sward structure. In: t'Mannetje L. and Jones R.M. (eds). *Field and Laboratory Methods for Grassland and Animal Production Research*. CABI Publishing, Wallingford, Oxon,. pp. 103-121.

LANTINGA E.A. NEUTEBOOM J.H. and MEIJS J.A.C. (2004). Sward methods. In: Penning P.D. (ed.). *Herbage Intake Handbook*. 2nd edn. British Grassland Society, pp. 23-52.

LEAVER J.D. (1982). *Herbage Intake Handbook.* British Grassland Society. 143 pp.

MANNETJE L. 't and JONES R.M. (2000). *Field and Laboratory Methods for Grassland and Animal Production Research.* CABI Publishing, Wallingford, Oxon. 447pp.

PENNING P.D. (2004). Animal based techniques for estimating herbage intake. In: Penning P.D. (ed). *Herbage Intake Handbook*. 2nd edn. British Grassland Society. pp. 53-93.

PENNING P.D. and RUTTER S.M. (2004). Ingestive behaviour. In: Penning P.D. (ed). *Herbage Intake Handbook* British Grassland Society. pp.151-175.

ROOK A.J. (2004). Statistical considerations in the design of herbage intake studies. In: Penning P.D.(ed). *Herbage Intake Handbook*. 2nd edn. British Grassland Society pp. 177-184.

TAYLOR J.A. (1993). Chairperson's summary paper. Session 18: Foraging strategy. *Proceedings of the 17th International Grassland Congress, New Zealand and Queensland,* February 1993. pp. 739-740.

# CHAPTER 2

# SWARD METHODS

### E.A. Lantinga, J.H. Neuteboom and J.A.C. Meijs

## 2.1 INTRODUCTION

Sward methods for measuring herbage intake are based on the same principle as for indoor experiments where intake is measured by difference:

herbage intake = herbage offered - herbage refused

The herbage mass (total mass of herbage per unit area of ground) is estimated at the beginning and at the end of the grazing period. The difference between the two gives an estimate of the apparent quantity of herbage consumed per unit area, but since the herbage may also grow during the grazing period a correction has to be applied to allow for this. The calculated consumption per unit area is then converted to intake per animal per day by dividing by the number of animal grazing days per unit area.

The measurement of herbage mass at the beginning and end of the grazing period can be achieved with reasonable accuracy, but the accurate measurement of herbage that may accumulate during grazing presents greater problems. Consequently, sward sampling methods are mainly applicable in systems where the grazing periods are relatively short, and where grazing pressures are high (i.e. paddock or strip grazing systems). Under these circumstances the amount of herbage that may accumulate during grazing will form only a relatively small proportion of the total herbage consumption, thus minimising the possibility of bias in estimating intake. However, attempts to measure herbage intake under intensive continuous grazing with dairy cows using sward-cutting techniques have proved to be successful (Deenen and Lantinga, 1993; Section 2.4)

Sward methods can only provide intake data on an individual-animal basis where animals are kept in individual plots. However, to obtain a normal grazing behaviour pattern and to reduce the labour requirement, intake studies are usually carried out with groups of animals. An advantage of the sward method is that the measurements also provide information on the herbage allowance (the weight of available herbage per unit of animal live weight) and the efficiency of grazing (herbage consumed expressed as a proportion of the herbage accumulated). In addition, chemical analysis of the samples taken allows pasture quality to be measured.

Methods of estimating herbage mass can be classified as destructive (cutting) or non-destructive. Cutting techniques usually involve the harvesting of a measured proportion of the area of pasture allotted to the animals and weighing and sampling the cut herbage. The amount of residual herbage (that remaining after grazing) is similarly determined. Non-destructive techniques usually involve the measurement of one or more sward characteristics in the grazing area before and after grazing, combined with a prediction of the herbage mass using an appropriate regression equation. This involves taking a limited number of cut samples to correlate with the sward characteristic (concomitant measures).

The potential for sward cutting techniques to provide reliable intake estimates depends on eliminating or minimising:

- possible systematic errors in estimating the difference between herbage mass at the start of grazing and at the end of grazing arising from the measurement technique;
- possible systematic errors in estimating the herbage accumulation during the grazing period;
- the random variation of the intake estimate, the precision of estimates depending on the variation in herbage mass within the pasture, on the method of sampling, and on the number, size and shape of the sample units.

The potential for concomitant measures to provide reliable intake estimates depends in addition on the possible systematic or random errors which may arise when applying the regression equation obtained between a variable (e.g. sward height) and the herbage mass, to estimate the mass of the pasture as a whole.

Reviews of literature on the subject of sward methods have been made by Brown (1954), 't Mannetje (1978, 2000), Meijs (1981) and Frame (1993). The intention in this chapter is: a) to give detailed descriptions of sward methods (including requirement for equipment and labour), b) to make a critical evaluation of the possible systematic and random errors, and c) to make an assessment of the relevance of the various methods available for particular experimental objectives.

## 2.2 METHODS OF ESTIMATING HERBAGE MASS

### 2.2.1 Sward-cutting techniques

The suitability of machinery for herbage sampling depends on the intended height of cutting, which in turn depends on the expected height of grazing. Frame (1993) gives detailed information about available cutting equipment for estimating herbage mass. In this chapter, three of the most useful cutting tools are described according to our and previous experience. Two of them have a cutting height of a few centimeters above ground level (motor scythe and a metallic frame with pins), whereas the last one has a cutting height very close to ground level (sheep-shearing head).

2.2.1.1 *Cutting above ground level* **Motor scythes** usually cut at a minimum height of about 4 cm and can vary in fingerbar width from 60 to 220 cm. They have a reciprocating knife which is actuated by a central rocker arm and can cut a swath with clearly defined edges without damaging the crop. Allen auto scythes and Agria motor scythes are often used for estimating intake in grazing experiments. Their value is largely limited to cattle-grazed swards. With the Agria the cutting height can be increased up to about 15 cm by using skids (Frame, 1993), but at increasing heights the mowing results can be disappointing due to a decreasing resistance of the herbage against cutting.

After cutting, the material has to be raked and put into containers, e.g. plastic bags. The length of the strips can be measured with a tape. The labour requirement per paddock, plot or field depends on the size, number and distribution of the sample units used. In experiments of Meijs (1981), 10 strips, 60 cm wide and 12 m long were cut per paddock (0.3 ha) with an Agria motor scythe at the start of each grazing period. The total field labour requirement when 10 strips were cut was approximately 1.5 man-hours (cutting 0.5, raking + collecting 0.75, measuring cut area 0.25 man-hours). Less time is needed to collect the smaller residues of post-grazing strips, but this is counterbalanced by the time required for removing faeces from the sampling area to be cut.

Advantages of a cutting height of 4 cm are:
a.  comparability of herbage mass with that of herbage cut for conservation;
b.  minimal soil contamination;
c.  minimal damage to the sward.

Disadvantages of motor scythes include the possibility of introducing bias due to:
a.  failure to sample below grazing height (especially at high levels of grazing intensity with beef cattle or sheep);
b.  flattening of herbage to below cutting height due to trampling, lying down of animals, faeces contamination and cutting or raking action;
c.  difference in cutting height between start and finish of grazing.

Several experiments have been reported indicating bias due to a), and some information concerning b) and c) was reported by Meijs (1981). In his studies the height of the stubble of the post-grazing strips was 0.43 cm longer than that of the pre-grazing strips, thus indicating the occurrence of bias b) and/or c). The stubble mass after cutting pre- and post-grazing strips with a motor scythe was compared by cutting the same strips again with a lawnmower (cutting width 50 cm, cutting height 3.1 or 3.5 cm, depending on type of machine). The stubble mass of the post-grazing strips cut by the lawnmower was on average 155 kg ha$^{-1}$ of organic matter higher than that of the pre-grazing strips. When it is assumed that this difference could be attributed completely to the longer stubble height of the post-grazing strips after cutting with the motor scythe, then this corresponds with a sward density of 360 kg OM ha$^{-1}$ cm$^{-1}$. This is unrealistically high for rotationally-grazed paddocks where perennial ryegrass is the dominant species. Observations during the experiments revealed that especially under dry conditions at the end of grazing the lawn mower sucks up considerable amounts of organic material from below cutting height (Lantinga, unpublished). Therefore, lawnmowers are no longer used in herbage intake research in the Netherlands since the early 1980s. Moreover, in the experiments of Meijs (1981) no collection box was installed behind the fingerbar, thus increasing the risk that not all of the cut material was collected by raking. Especially in short vegetations, e.g. at the end of a grazing period, collection boxes are indispensable. Approximately similar cutting heights before and after grazing can be achieved when the knife of the motor mower is always as sharp as possible and the fingerbar is pushed to the ground during the mowing operation.

A **metallic frame with pins** can be used in case where no motor scythe is available or grazing occurs below the minimum cutting height of the motor scythe (Figure 2.1). This frame was developed at Wageningen Agricultural University in the 1960s by the second author and the cutting area is 50 * 50 cm or smaller. The frame has one side with a loose pin. This side can be moved easily in the stubble of the sward when a small strip of grass is cut beforehand in front of the area to be harvested. The frame is closed

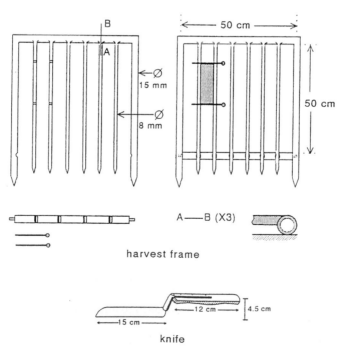

*Figure 2.1. The metallic harvesting frame with attached and loose pins together with the spinach knife for cutting the grass.*

before harvesting by attaching the loose pin. The herbage is cut with a spinach knife just above the metal pins. The cutting area can be made smaller by using extra (smaller) loose pins. It takes about one hour to harvest 10 samples of 50 * 50 cm.

The advantages of this metallic frame are:

a. the harvested area is very precise through the use of attached pins at the bottom of the sward;
b. it facilitates a reproducible cutting height of about 3 cm under all conditions;
c. plant material pressed down to the ground by trampling etc. can be teased upwards easily before cutting;
d. no soil contamination;
e. subsampling is not necessary for dry matter determination;
f. dry matter yields can be easily correlated with sward height measurements using plate meters with a diameter of 50 cm.

A disadvantage is that it is difficult to cut and collect herbage in intensively-grazed swards.

From observations in different types of pastures it appears that the yield coefficient of variation was on average in the order of 20% in case of cutting areas of 50 * 50 cm. Assuming a mean herbage mass of 2500 kg DM ha$^{-1}$, then this indicates a standard deviation of 500 kg DM ha$^{-1}$. In order to detect differences (P<0.05) of 10%, it would then be necessary to harvest about 35 plots per paddock [LSD = 2.05 * $\sqrt{2}$ * (500/$\sqrt{n}$)]. This large number (n) of plots to be harvested makes it worthwhile to combine the cuttings with height measurements in a double sampling technique (Section 2.2.2).

2.2.1.2 *Cutting close to ground level*. The simplest cutting devices are hand-operated tools such as shears, scissors and knives. These require a high labour input but have the advantage that height of cutting can be accurately controlled especially when rough or trampled areas are to be harvested. However, individuals can vary in the height they consider representative of ground level. Therefore it is advisable that pre- and post grazing strips are sampled by the same operator.

To reduce labour requirements, hand-held power-driven tools such as hedge trimmers and sheep-shearing heads are commonly used. Hedge-trimmers have the following disadvantages:

a. they do not cut at ground level and are not generally equipped with collecting trays;
b. post-grazing samples may be cut to a lower level than pre-grazing ones (Alder and Minson, 1963);
c. they require frequent overhaul and replacement of cutter-bar assemblies.

The **sheep-shearing head** is less difficult to maintain in good cutting order and is capable of cutting closer to ground level than the hedge trimmer. Reliable results can be obtained with an electrically operated sheep-shearing head (Walters and Evans, 1979). Within each paddock six pre- and six post grazing strips, each measuring approximately 7.6 cm wide and 25 m long, are cut as close to ground level as possible taking care to avoid undue soil contamination. Taking six sample strips per paddock (0.05 ha) requires approximately 1 man-hour. For ten strips (e.g. on an area of 0.3 ha comparable with the paddocks used with the cutting equipment as described in Section 2.2.1.1) the labour requirement is about 1.7 man-hours.

Advantages of the sheep-shearing head are:
a.   no herbage can be grazed below the cutting level;
b.   a reproducible cutting height before and after grazing can be achieved.

General disadvantages are:
a.   comparison with estimates of herbage mass harvested at different times during the season by a machine cutting for conservation is difficult, and may preclude the possibility of calculating whole season yields;
b.   high level of soil contamination and dead material;
c.   damage to the sward.

Under certain conditions the following difficulties have been encountered when using the sheep-shearing head:
a.   on uneven ground some root growth may be cut and included in the sample, and under these conditions samples cut with cordless grass shears may be preferable to the sheep-shearing head (Matches, 1963);
b.   the amount of dead organic material included in the sample may vary depending on weather conditions;
c.   losses can occur in recovering post-grazed samples from swards showing a prostrate habit of growth;
d.   a considerable and varying amount of herbage is harvested from the sward layer where no consumption occurs (the biomass below a sward height of 4 cm may vary between 2000 and 3500 kg DM ha$^{-1}$ in grazed paddocks);
e.   overestimation of the factor for calculating herbage accumulation during grazing (see Section 2.3).

To avoid problems due to differential soil contamination all herbage mass data should be expressed on an organic matter basis.

2.2.1.3 *Comparison between cutting methods* A comparison and summary of the important aspects of the three cutting equipment categories is shown in Table 2.1. All three techniques are one-step cutting systems.

2.2.2 Double sampling method (concomitant measures)

Concomitant measures are often used in pasture sampling to reduce labour requirement or to improve precision (Back *et al.*, 1969; O'Sullivan *et al.*, 1987). The general principle is to make the indirect observations (e.g. sward height) on a substantial number of sites within the plot and to make the direct measurements on some of them (correlative observations). The regression of the direct on the indirect

*Table 2.1. Comparison of three cutting techniques. References: Motor scythe (Meijs, 1981;*
*Lantinga, unpublished), Sheep-shearing head (Walters and Evans, 1979), Metallic frame with*
*pins (Neuteboom, unpublished). + is positive aspect, - is negative aspect.*

| Cutting equipment | Motor scythe | Sheep-shearing head | Metallic frame |
|---|---|---|---|
| Cutting height (cm) | ±4 | ±0 | ±3 |
| Cutting width (m) | 0.60 | 0.08 | 0.50 |
| Cutting length (m) | 12 | 25 | 0.50 |
| Cutting area per plot (m$^2$) | 7.2 | 2.0 | 0.25 |
| Man hours per 10 samples | 1.5 | 1.7 | 1.0 |
| Avoiding grazing below cutting height | - | + | ± |
| Achieving comparable stubble pre/post-grazing | ± | + | + |
| Low soil contamination | + | - | + |
| Little damage to the sward | + | - | + |
| Calculating accumulation factor (2.3) | + | - | + |

measurements is determined and in case of a linear relationship the mean paddock yield is read off at the mean of the indirect measurements.

The various non-destructive techniques for the indirect observations have been reviewed by Brown (1954), 't Mannetje (1978, 2000) and Frame (1993), and may be classified as follows:

a.    height measurements and weighted-disc methods (plate meters);
b.    electronic capacitance probes;
c.    visual estimates;
c.    point quadrats.

When using these techniques it is recommended that for each sampling set calibrations are made to minimise bias. Visual estimates and point quadrats can not be regarded as critical research methods for estimating intake, due mainly to their liability to bias. At best they can provide a rough guide to grazing intake where pastures are relatively homogeneous and conditions are uniform, and where large differences are expected in herbage mass between the start and end of grazing. Many versions of simple weighted-disc instruments have been developed. The disc, normally consisting of a light aluminum, plastic or tempex plate, fits over a rod held in a vertical position with its base at ground level. It may be allowed to settle to a constant position on the sward (falling-plate meter) or alternatively the rod may be pushed down to the ground and the disc is supported above ground level by the sward (rising-plate meter). According to Carlier *et al.* (1989) the level of precision that can be obtained with the rising-plate meter and the capacitance probe is about the same, despite improvements established with the capacitance probe in New Zealand (Vickery *et al.*, 1980). In a comparative evaluation of a rising-plate meter and a capacitance meter, Michell (1982) and Michell and Large (1983) found that the plate meter was marginally more accurate than the capacitance meter.

The value of the double sampling technique will be illustrated with data from a very heterogeneous extensively-grazed pasture with a diverse botanical composition. The harvesting equipment was the metal frame with pins described in Section 2.2.1.1. and harvested area per plot was 0.25 m² (0.5 * 0.5 m). With a group of students, 40 plots were harvested and the dry matter yield was correlated with height measurements taken with a falling-plate meter (r=0.78). The heterogeneity was reflected in a high yield coefficient of variation (46.5%). The average herbage mass in the 40 plots was 2790 kg DM ha⁻¹ with a standard deviation of 1298 kg DM ha⁻¹. This corresponds with a standard error of the mean of 205 kg DM ha⁻¹ (1298/√40). Using systematic sampling, 90 height measurements were done in the paddock. The average sward height (H) was 14.63 cm with a standard deviation of 3.92 cm. The precision of herbage mass estimation was analysed with the following formula (McIntyre, 1978):

$$S_{\hat{y}} = \sqrt{\frac{S_{H.Y}^2}{N_c} + \frac{S_H^2 * b^2}{N_m}} \qquad (2.1)$$

where:
$S_{\hat{y}}$ is the s.e. of an estimate of herbage mass
$S_{H.Y}^2$ is the residual variability of the calibration equation $[=(1-0.78^2) * 1298^2]$
$S_H^2$ is the variability of measurement of H $(=3.92^2)$
b is the regression coefficient of the calibration equation $(=167)$
$N_c$ is the number of calibration points in the regression $(=40)$
$N_m$ is the number of meter readings taken $(=90)$

The s.e. of the estimate of herbage mass $S_{\hat{y}}$ could thus be calculated as 147 kg DM ha⁻¹, i.e. a reduction of about 30%. In other words, when the aim is to achieve an s.e. of about 200 kg DM ha⁻¹, this could have been obtained by taking 90 height measurements in the paddock and harvesting only 20 plots with concomitant height measurements instead of 40 cuttings. Such a number of height measurements can be easily done within half an hour in a paddock with an area of about 5 ha. It can also be calculated that with an infinitive number of height measurements $N_m$ the s.e. will be lowered to 130 kg DM ha⁻¹.

## 2.3 HERBAGE ACCUMULATION AND HERBAGE INTAKE DURING A ROTATIONAL GRAZING PERIOD

The sward cutting technique without correction for herbage accumulation during grazing is only applicable when the grazing period is very short and relatively large amounts of material are eaten per unit area during the period (Meijs et al., 1982). In this situation herbage accumulation during the period of grazing (disturbed accumulation) is negligible in relation to the total amount of herbage consumed and can thus be reasonably ignored when calculating intake. However, when grazing takes place over an extended period (more than one day), herbage accumulation during grazing cannot be ignored. The disturbed accumulation cannot be measured directly since it is constantly being influenced by the grazing animal. Sward $CO_2$ assimilation measurements might be an alternative approach (Lantinga, 1985b). However, this method is laborious and very expensive. It is therefore normally measured indirectly from an estimate of the rate of undisturbed herbage accumulation during the grazing period in exclosures. This estimate is then used to calculate disturbed accumulation using an equation relating disturbed and undisturbed accumulation (see below). Under potential growing conditions (ample supply of water and nutrients) the rate of undisturbed herbage accumulation of closed swards (LAI $\geq$ 4) can also be estimated with a descriptive growth model when global radiation data are available (derived from Lantinga, 1988):

$$\Delta Y_u = \Delta Y_{u,max} * (1 - \exp(1 - \exp(-\varepsilon R_g / \Delta Y_{u,max}))) - 15 \qquad (2.2)$$

where:
$\Delta Y_u$ is undisturbed herbage accumulation rate (kg DM ha$^{-1}$ d$^{-1}$);
$\Delta Y_{u,max}$ is maximum undisturbed herbage accumulation rate (kg DM ha$^{-1}$ d$^{-1}$);
$\varepsilon$ is initial radiation use efficiency (kg DM ha$^{-1}$ / (MJ m$^{-2}$));
$R_g$ is daily incoming global radiation (MJ m$^{-2}$ d$^{-1}$).

Values for $\Delta Y_{u,max}$ and $\varepsilon$ show a seasonal variation and can be read from Figure 2.2. The underlying explanatory simulation model takes into account (i) the composition of the incoming radiation (direct vs. diffuse fluxes), (ii) the shift from reproductive to vegetative growth in late spring, (iii) the decreasing rate of maximum leaf gross $CO_2$ assimilation with decreasing radiation in late summer and autumn, and (iv) the generally lower initial light-use efficiency of leaves in late summer and autumn due to crown rust and an increasing fraction of senescing leaves in the lop layers of the canopy.

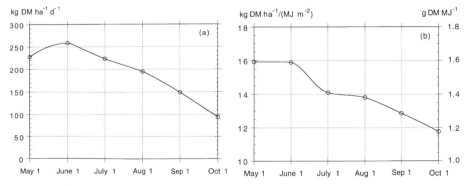

*Figure 2.2. Seasonal course of (a) the maximum undisturbed herbage accumulation rate of closed canopies ($\Delta Y_{u,max}$) and (b) the initial radiation use efficiency ($\varepsilon$) in North-western Europe.*

An estimate of the rate of undisturbed accumulation during grazing can be calculated from estimates of the herbage mass at the beginning and at the end of the grazing period as follows:

1. Under cages (one sample in each cage).

   Cages are commonly 4.2 m long and 1.2 m wide; more details about design and materials used are given by 't Mannetje (1978). Bias may arise if herbage is protected by a cage for any length of time due to the protection from grazing and the abnormal microclimate within the cage resulting in a herbage accumulation not typical for the rest of the sward. The magnitude of this effect is directly related to the length of time the cages are in a given position ('t Mannetje, 1978). However, if the grazing period is shorter than one week this effect is insignificant. Further disadvantage of cages are:

   - their fixed size, especially if it is intended that sample units for the pre- and post-grazing yields in the grazed paddock should take the form of long strips;
   - the degree of correspondence of herbage yields under the cages at the start of grazing and the measured yields in the paired pre-grazing strips;
   - their influence on the behaviour of the animals possibly leading to sward damage in the vicinity of the cages and thus in the area allotted to the post-grazing strips.

2. In fenced areas (allowing several samples from each fenced area).

   Often one or two areas are fenced off within the pasture and in each exclosure a number of samples are cut pre- and post-grazing. Advantages of using large fenced-off areas include a wider choice of the area to cut at each sample site (this is especially important when cutting is mechanized) and minimal bias since the effect of fencing on microclimate of the sward exclosures is negligible. As a result of fencing-off only one or a few relatively large parts of the grazed area, there is a possibility of siting the exclosures in non-representative areas of the pasture. However, since absolute measurements of herbage mass are not required this should not create a serious problem. When the sward in the exclosures has reached a certain leaf area index (about 4) herbage accumulation (undisturbed) is almost independent of level of herbage mass, thus reducing the possibility of bias due to non-representative siting of exclosures.

The disturbed herbage accumulation in the grazed area will be lower than the undisturbed accumulation in the exclosure due to defoliation (reduction of leaf area index leading to reduction in light interception), treading, and faeces contamination. Thus, disturbed accumulation = g * undisturbed accumulation. The herbage consumed when a correction is applied for the disturbed herbage accumulation can then be calculated:

$$C = (Y_s - Y_e) + g \cdot \Delta Y_u \qquad (2.3)$$

where:

C is herbage consumed (kg DM ha$^{-1}$);

$Y_s$ is herbage mass at the start of a grazing period (kg DM ha$^{-1}$);
$Y_e$ is herbage mass at the end of a grazing period (kg DM ha$^{-1}$);
$\Delta Y_u$ is undisturbed herbage accumulation in exclosure during a grazing period
(kg DM ha$^{-1}$).
Herbage mass refers to the sward layer above a cutting height of approximately 4
cm (Meijs et al., 1982).

Linehan et al. (1947) assumed that at every moment of a rotational grazing period
both the rate of consumption of herbage and the rate of herbage accumulation are
proportional to the quantity of uneaten herbage at that moment. Thus, they arrived at
the following equation for the consumption of herbage:

$$C = (Y_s - Y_e) \ \frac{\ln (Y_u/Y_e)}{\ln (Y_s/Y_e)} \tag{2.4}$$

where $Y_u$ is herbage mass at the end of a grazing period in exclosure (kg DM ha$^{-1}$).

When equations (2.3) and (2.4) are combined, the accumulation factor g (Equation
2.2) can be calculated:

$$g = \frac{(Y_s - Y_e)}{(Y_u - Y_s)} \left( \frac{\ln (Y_u/Y_e)}{\ln (Y_s/Y_e)} - 1 \right) \tag{2.5}$$

In fact, Linehan's formula is based on four simplifying assumptions about the rate
of herbage accumulation and the rate of herbage intake (Lantinga, 1985a). These are:
•   Growth of the ungrazed grass in the exclosure is exponential at all stages of
    development, independent of the leaf area index. This assumption is not correct.
    Already in the 1950s it had been found that during regrowth the rate of herbage
    accumulation increases more or less exponentially until complete light
    interception is approached (leaf area index is then about 4), and that thereafter this
    rate is almost constant (Brougham, 1956). This feature has been described
    mathematically by Goudriaan and Monteith (1990) with the expolinear growth
    equation.
•   The rate of herbage accumulation during the grazing period is proportional to the
    quantity of uneaten herbage above cutting height. Although for the greater part of
    the grazing period there is a nearly closed canopy, this might be a correct
    assumption because the leaves with the greatest assimilatory capacity are grazed
    first.
•   There is no net contribution of the stubble to the production capacity of the sward,
    since only the herbage yield above cutting height is taken into account. In the
    experiments of Linehan et al. (1947) the cutting height was between 3 and 4 cm.
    In reality the assimilatory capacity of the stubble below this cutting height can be
    considerable, especially in spring, and its carbon balance may be positive.
•   There is a negative exponential intake pattern over the grazing period. This
    assumption seems reasonable, except at extreme high levels of herbage allowance.

These four assumptions have been evaluated by Lantinga (1985a) by means of dynamic simulation, with measured sward $CO_2$ assimilation/light-response curves as the main input. In the simulation model, the rate of gross $CO_2$ assimilation at any moment of a grazing period is calculated in such a way that herbage mass controls the assimilatory capacity of the sward. For the evaluation, curves were used for grazing cycles in spring (May) and summer (August). The curves concern ungrazed, partly-grazed and completely-grazed herbage. These grazing stages refer to the fractions of the initial herbage mass above a 4cm stubble removed by grazing cattle. For intermediate values of the herbage mass, the required curves were obtained using linear interpolation. The justification of this procedure is shown in Figure 2.3. A similar linear relationship has also been reported by King et al. (1984). The reason is that with the onset of grazing the young leaves with the highest assimilation potential are removed first, thus causing a greater decrease in sward $CO_2$ assimilation than would be expected on the basis of light interception. Figure 2.3 shows that, especially in the spring sward, the stubble below the reference height of 4 cm has some assimilatory capacity. However, this capacity does not reflect the large amount of herbage present here. In normally treated, rotationally grazed swards this layer contains about 3000 kg DM ha$^{-1}$. However, the amount of green material is very small, especially in autumn, and moreover, these leaves and sheaths show little activity. For the description of the simulation of respiration, growth, dry matter distribution, death of plant tissue see Lantinga (1985a). Since at the onset of grazing in both grazing cycles the leaf area index was greater than 4, it was assumed that in the undisturbed situation the assimilatory capacity of the sward remains unchanged during the grazing period. This resulted in simulated rates of undisturbed herbage accumulation almost linearly

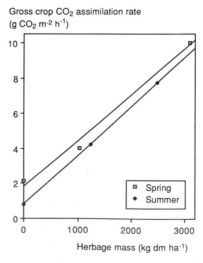

*Figure 2.3. Relationship between herbage mass above a 4cm stubble height and gross crop $CO_2$ assimilation rate of a perennial ryegrass sward in spring and summer at 800 W m$^{-2}$ (400-3000 nm) (After Lantinga, 1985a).*

dependent on time when the daily global radiation and mean temperature where kept constant. In the approach of Linehan et al. (1947) an exponential growth pattern was assumed during this growth stage. Therefore, the simulated rates of herbage accumulation at the start of a grazing period were always higher than were inherently assumed in the equation of Linehan et al. (1947). It will be clear that this discrepancy increases with an increasing difference between $Y_s$ and $Y_u$, i.e. with increasing length of the grazing period. Consequently, herbage accumulation during grazing and thus herbage intake, will be underestimated to a larger extent with increasing length of the grazing period using Linehan's equation.

The rate of herbage intake at any time of a grazing period was calculated using a negative exponential asymptotic relationship between herbage allowance and herbage intake (Zemmelink, 1980):

$$I = I_m (1-e^{-(A/I_m)^h})^{1/h} \tag{2.6}$$

where:
I is daily herbage intake (kg DM cow$^{-1}$ d$^{-1}$);
$I_m$ is maximum daily herbage intake (kg DM cow$^{-1}$ d$^{-1}$);
A is daily herbage allowance (kg DM cow$^{-1}$ d$^{-1}$);
h is shape parameter (-).

Linehan et al. (1947) assumed a linear relationship between the quantity of uneaten herbage above cutting height and the rate of herbage intake. It appeared, however, that even at a high herbage allowance of more than 30 kg DM cow$^{-1}$ d$^{-1}$, the difference between the intake patterns over a grazing period of three days were so small that only minor effects on rate of herbage accumulation can be expected as a result of using either one or the other function.

Comparisons between Linehan's equation and the simulation output revealed that for short grazing periods up to about three days and a relative high herbage mass at the start of grazing as in Figure 2.3 (more than 2500 kg DM ha$^{-1}$) the calculated daily herbage intakes differed little (below 5%). However, for situations with an initial herbage mass between 1000 and 1500 kg DM ha$^{-1}$ the differences were significant. For instance, for a young spring sward it was found that at a herbage allowance of 29.5 kg DM cow$^{-1}$ d$^{-1}$, the herbage intake according to Linehan's equation was 13.9 kg DM cow$^{-1}$ d$^{-1}$, whereas the simulation model predicted 15.5 kg DM cow$^{-1}$ d$^{-1}$. The reason is that in such swards the difference between $Y_s$ and $Y_u$ becomes relatively large, even for short grazing periods of three days. A new formula was therefore developed to measure herbage intake in a better way using sward-cutting techniques for all situations of rotational grazing. For this purpose it was assumed that in the ungrazed situation herbage accumulation is linear rather than exponential (Figure 2.4). The other assumptions made by Linehan et al. (1947) were kept unchanged as confirmed by experiment. Using these assumptions, Lantinga (1985a) derived an improved formula, namely:

$$C = (Y_s - Y_e) + \left( \frac{1-(Y_e/Y_s)}{-\ln(Y_e/Y_s)} \right) (Y_u - Y_s) \tag{2.7}$$

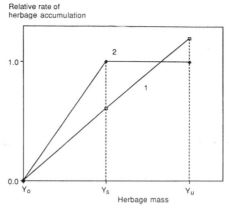

*Figure 2.4. Relationship between the relative rate of herbage accumulation and the herbage mass above a 4cm stubble height as assumed by Linehan (line 1) and by Lantinga (1985; line 2). $Y_s$ is herbage mass at start of grazing; $Y_u$ is herbage mass at the end of grazing in an undisturbed area.*

The multiplication term between brackets in Equation 2.7 is the accumulation factor g as defined in Equation 2.3. The performance of this new equation in comparison with the model output was excellent for both a wide range of herbage allowance levels (Lantinga, 1985a) and number of grazing days (Table 2.2).

Equation 2.7 may not be used when herbage mass is determined with sheep-shearing heads. In this case the herbage accumulation factor g will be heavily overestimated due to the inclusion of the stubble mass below a sward height of 4 cm in the herbage yields. This is clear from Figure 2.5, where for two reference sward heights (0 and 4 cm) the relationship between the relative grazing residue and the herbage accumulation factor is shown. For the calculations it has been assumed that the amount of dry matter between 0 and 4 cm equals 2750 kg DM ha$^{-1}$.

*Table 2.2. Influence of the length of the grazing period on the rate of herbage intake calculated with the simulation model, Equation 2.7 and Linehan's formula (Equation 2.4). Conditions: spring sward; herbage mass at start of grazing 3105 kg DM ha$^{-1}$; herbage allowance 32.5 kg DM cow$^{-1}$ d$^{-1}$.*

| Grazing period (days) | Herbage intake (kg DM cow$^{-1}$ d$^{-1}$) | | |
|---|---|---|---|
| | Simulation model | Equation 2.7 | Linehan |
| 3 | 16.1 | 16.1 | 15.5 |
| 7 | 16.1 | 16.0 | 13.9 |

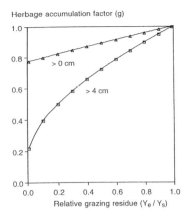

*Figure 2.5. Dependence of herbage accumulation factor (g) on the relative grazing residue as influenced by the reference sward height for herbage mass determination. Calculated values from Equation 2.7.*

## 2.4 HERBAGE PRODUCTION AND HERBAGE INTAKE UNDER CONTINUOUS GRAZING

Continuous grazing and rotational grazing differ, not only in the way herbage is consumed, but also in the physiology of herbage production. Under controlled continuous grazing, resulting in a more or less constant sward height throughout time, there is a balance between production and consumption. During a rotational grazing period, consumption is in general much greater than accumulation of herbage. According to Frame (1993) estimates of herbage production on continuously-stocked swards are best made using techniques of tissue turnover (Bircham and Hodgson, 1983; Davies, 1993) or carbon exchange methods (Parsons *et al.*, 1984; Lantinga, 1985b; Davies, 1993). Estimates of herbage production using cage techniques have to be interpreted with care since it is important to realise that, the further the herbage mass diverges from that in the sward, the less valuable the measurements will be. Parsons *et al.* (1984) observed a marked increase in the rate of $CO_2$ assimilation under cages over a period of about three weeks during which leaf area index increased from about 1 to 5. The net accumulation of herbage under a cage depends on the extent to which any increase in $CO_2$ assimilation and gross herbage production is offset by a subsequent increase in the rate of tissue death (Parsons *et al.*, 1984). In more leniently grazed swards, ceiling yields may be reached under a cage before the end of a measurement period and, in decreasing light environment such as in the autumn, this will result in zero or negative growth. Despite these warnings, cage techniques are still being used to measure herbage production and herbage intake under continuous grazing using sampling intervals of 2 or 3 weeks (e.g. Davies *et al.*, 1993, Lee *et al.*, 2001). Frame (1993) concluded that in a sward grazed to a fixed height by variable stocking, the stocking rate itself can give useful indications of patterns of herbage production. Deenen and Lantinga (1993) have used an adapted cage technique with sampling intervals of 1 to 2 weeks to estimate herbage intake in swards continuously grazed with dairy cows. They observed only small differences in the seasonal pattern and absolute level of net energy intake calculated from animal performance and herbage accumulation under exclosure cages. For the comparison, herbage accumulation and intake were expressed in Dutch Feed Units (Van Es, 1978). One Dutch Feed Unit (VEM) contains 6.9 kJ NE for lactation. Averaged over the growing season, herbage dry matter accumulated in growth periods of up to one month contains about 1000 VEM kg$^{-1}$ DM (Meijs, 1981). The energy content of herbage samples was calculated as follows (Van Es, 1978):

$$E_h = \{0.6 + 0.0024 \left( \frac{ME}{44} - 57 \right) \} \frac{0.975\ ME}{1.65} \tag{2.8}$$

where:
$E_h$ is energy content of the herbage (VEM kg$^{-1}$ DM);
ME is Metabolizable Energy (kcal kg$^{-1}$ DM);
$\quad$ ME = 3.4 DOM + 1.4 CP $\tag{2.9}$
DOM is Digestible Organic Matter (g kg$^{-1}$ DM);
CP is Crude Protein (g kg$^{-1}$ DM).

Estimates of herbage accumulation were obtained using the double-sampling technique. Before the exclosure cages were placed (10 per paddock; 4.2 m long and 1.2 m wide), initial herbage mass was estimated on basis of the initial mean herbage height in the plot (10 readings with a falling-plate meter; diameter 50 cm, pressure 1.7 kg m$^{-2}$) and regression between mean herbage height and herbage mass in strips parallel to the exclosure cage. Using the same double sampling technique herbage mass in the whole paddock was estimated with the average herbage height on the paddock as an estimator (40 readings per paddock). The growth period under the exclosure cages was one week in spring and early summer and gradually extended to two weeks in October. In the continuously-grazed paddocks the 'put-and-take' method was used to maintain a target mean herbage height of 7 cm throughout the grazing season. Patches of rejected grass were cut regularly in order to minimise the area of leniently-grazed herbage. After each growth period cages were moved and the procedure was repeated. Based on growth curves determined by Parsons et al. (1984) it can be assumed than in a sward released from continuous grazing, grass growth is more or less exponential. Therefore Linehan's formula may be used to estimate herbage intake from herbage accumulation data under cages:

$$C = (Y_t - Y_{t+1}) \frac{\ln\{(Y_t + \Delta Y_u)/Y_{t+1}\}}{\ln(Y_t/Y_{t+1})} \tag{2.10}$$

where:
C is herbage intake (kVEM ha$^{-1}$);
$Y_t$ is herbage mass in the paddock at time t (kVEM ha$^{-1}$);
$Y_{t+1}$ is herbage mass in the paddock at time t+1 (kVEM ha$^{-1}$);
$\Delta Y_u$ is herbage accumulation under the exclosure cage from t to t+1 (kVEM ha$^{-1}$).

Herbage mass refers to the sward layer above a reference height of 2 cm, since the daily carbon exchange of a continuously-grazed sward with an average herbage height of about 7 cm is in balance at about this sward height (Lantinga, unpublished). This is closer to ground level than in rotationally-grazed swards due to a more leafy stubble. However, the average cutting height with the Agria motor scythe was about 4 cm. From a number of separate harvests with a spinach knife below this cutting height it was found that the amount of dry matter in the sward layer from 2 to 4 cm is about 1000 kg DM ha$^{-1}$. This amount was added to the herbage masses determined by cutting for calculation of the herbage intake with Equation 2.10. The total herbage intake calculated in this way compared with the level calculated from animal performance data was 8% lower at a fertilizer N input of 250 kg ha$^{-1}$ yr$^{-1}$ and 4% higher at 550 kg N ha$^{-1}$ yr$^{-1}$ (Table 2.3). The difference between the two N input levels might be due to an underestimation of the herbage ME content according to Equation 7 at low and moderate N input levels (see Deenen and Lantinga, 1993).

*Table 2.3. Total herbage intake under continuous grazing with dairy cows calculated from animal performance data (method 1) and from herbage accumulation under exclosure cages according to Equation 2.10 (method 2). Relative figures per fertilizer N level between brackets. Source: Deenen and Lantinga (1993).*

| Fertilizer N (kg ha$^{-1}$) | Herbage intake (kVEM ha$^{-1}$) | |
| --- | --- | --- |
| | Method 1 | Method 2 |
| 250 | 7849 (100) | 7200 ( 92) |
| 550 | 11107 (100) | 11503 (104) |

## 2.5 PRECISION OF ESTIMATION OF HERBAGE MASS AND CONSUMPTION

The precision of the estimate describes how close on average the estimate is to the mean value. A measure for the precision is the standard error. The difference between the mean value of the possible estimates and the true value of the quantity to be estimated is the bias (the systematic error). Some causes of bias have been discussed in Sections 2.2 and 2.3.

In many cases the 'best' estimating procedure is the one that produces a sufficiently precise estimate in the cheapest way (minimising cost of labour, machinery, laboratory), but it is important to understand the causes of variability so that the estimating procedure can be improved.

An estimate of intake derived by a sward method, is a function of estimates of the herbage mass of the pasture obtained by cutting parts of the pasture (the sampling units). The sampling procedure is the way the sampling units are selected, and the choice of the number, size and shape of these units. The precision of the estimate of the herbage mass apart from measurement error is determined by the spatial distribution of the herbage mass of the pasture (the heterogeneity of the sward) and the estimating procedure. The choice of sampling procedure has to be such that the best estimate of the herbage mass of the pasture is achieved. In estimating intake, the herbage mass of the same pasture is measured at different times and under different conditions (pre- and post-grazing). Therefore it is often advantageous to select the sampling units close together (paired sampling units).

When comparing the intake for different treatments, estimates from different pastures, possibly from different groups of animals in different periods have to be used. Possible variations then also include those concerned with the intake of an animal on different pastures (with the same treatment), and in the mean intake of different groups of animals. The standard error of the estimate therefore should not be used uncritically for the comparison of treatments. From indoor experiments where the intake for separate animals can be estimated accurately, some information can be obtained about the variation in intake between animals. Also, from repetitions of intake measurements, the standard error of the estimate (including variation in intake for different pastures) can be estimated.

### 2.5.1 Estimation of herbage mass

2.5.1.1 *Some factors affecting variation in herbage mass and herbage intake.* The precision of the estimate of herbage mass will be adversely affected by heterogeneity of the sward. This heterogeneity is caused by variation within the pasture of factors which influence herbage accumulation, such as:
- botanical composition: large differences can exist in the accumulation of herbage between species and varieties under the same growing conditions;
- soil structure and composition: the borders of a pasture may produce less herbage due to intensive treading and overriding;
- supply of fertilizers and water: if the distribution of water and fertilizers is not uniform over the total grazed area, the variation in herbage mass will increase.

Towards the end of a grazing period increased heterogeneity of the sward can be caused by factors which influence herbage intake or accumulation such as:
- selection by animals between herbage species or plant parts;
- selection by animals between clean and faeces contaminated herbage;
- treading of herbage by the grazing animals.

The degree of selection can be decreased when lower levels of herbage allowance are applied by forcing the animals to become less selective. The intensity of grazing thus has an influence on the variation of residual herbage. At the end of a grazing period the variation in herbage mass is higher than when the area has been cut. This variation in residual herbage and the variation in the return of nutrients by local urine and faeces excretion will increase variation in herbage mass of the regrowth.

The precision of the herbage intake estimated by the sward cutting technique can be improved when using aftermath or topped pre-grazed pastures. On homogeneous swards the precision of the estimation of herbage intake can be improved with a high level of herbage mass at the beginning of grazing and a low level of residual herbage at the end of grazing.

2.5.1.2 *The spatial distribution of herbage mass*. The herbage mass at a point in the pasture can be visualised as the herbage mass per unit area in a (small) square with this point as the centre. The spatial distribution can be visualised as a contour map, the contour lines connecting neighbouring points with the same herbage mass (Meijs *et al.*, 1982). In practice, the spatial distribution of the herbage mass in the pasture is not known otherwise there would be no sampling problem, but some general features may be known e.g. whether there are trends in one or two directions (fertility, drainage pipes, etc.) and how rapidly the herbage mass changes between points.

2.5.1.3. *Useful types of sampling*. The type of sampling is the way the sample (i.e. the n units for which the measurements are to be obtained) is selected out of the total population of sampling units. Useful types arc simple random sampling, stratified random sampling and systematic sampling. In these types of sampling, concomitant measures may be used to improve the estimate (these are non-destructive techniques as listed in Section 2.2.2). Double sampling, ranked set sampling and sampling by the method of Jones and Haydock (1970) are potentially unbiased sampling techniques using concomitant measures.

**Simple random sampling** means selecting the n sampling units at random out of the population of possible sampling units. The estimate of the herbage mass of the pasture is the sample mean and the estimate of the population standard deviation is the sample standard deviation.

In **stratified random sampling**, groups of possible sampling units (the strata) in the population are formed first, followed by simple random sampling for each of the strata. The estimate of the herbage mass of the pasture is the weighted sample mean from the different strata (weighted according to the size of the strata), and the estimate of the standard deviation is the square root of the weighted mean of sample standard deviations in the different strata (weighted according to the number of samples in the strata). The best choice of stratification is where differences between strata are large and the variation between the possible units in the strata are small.

In **systematic sampling**, the n sampling units are not selected with a random procedure, but are units at regular positions in the pasture, possibly with a random starting position. The estimate of the herbage mass is the same as with simple random sampling. There is in general no unbiased estimate of the precision. However a common estimate of the precision is the sample standard deviation, as in simple random sampling.

In **double sampling**, a quantitative concomitant variable is measured on many randomly selected sampling units while on a few of these (the reference samples) the herbage mass is also measured. By regression the relation between the herbage mass and the concomitant variable is estimated and the regression equation is used to estimate the herbage mass on all units where the concomitant variable has been measured. Although non bias in the procedure is only guaranteed if the reference samples are selected randomly, it is still advisable to select the reference samples to represent the range of levels of herbage mass present. For the estimation of herbage mass and the precision see Sections 2.2.2 and 2.5.3.

In **ranked set sampling**, k sets of k units are selected by simple random sampling (possibly within strata). The concomitant measures for these units are used to rank the units within the sets. The sampling units for which the herbage mass will be measured are the unit with rank 1 in set 1, the unit with rank 2 in set 2, etc. The whole procedure may then be repeated, say m times, so that the sample then consists of m*k units. The estimate of the herbage mass is the same as with simple random sampling. The standard error of this estimate is:

$$\sqrt{(\frac{1}{k} \sum_1^k s_{(i)}^2 )}$$
(2.11)

where:

$s_{(i)}$ is the standard deviation of the m observations with rank i.

Jones and Haydock (1970) described a sampling method in which after first measuring a concomitant variable on a large number of randomly chosen units, the herbage mass is measured by cutting 3 units with the mean (or nearest to the mean) value for the concomitant variable. The mean of these three observations is an estimate of the mean herbage mass of the pasture. However, with this procedure the precision cannot be estimated.

Simple and stratified random sampling produce unbiased estimates of the herbage mass of the pasture. Systematic sampling may produce a biased estimate of the herbage mass when the regularity in the sampling scheme and the regularity in the spatial distribution coincide. If the standard deviation from a systematic sample is estimated as if it were a simple random sample, it is usually overestimated (Cochran, 1977). Nevertheless, systematic sampling is often used in practice when no estimate of the precision is needed. Selecting the sample is easily organised and in many situations it produces a precise estimate of the herbage mass. The use of concomitant information in double sampling is advantageous when the concomitant variable is highly correlated with the herbage mass. Ranked set sampling compared with simple random sampling reduces the required sample size by a factor slightly less than 1/2*(k + 1), when the ranking within sets is perfect. This procedure is particularly useful if the ranking can be achieved in a simple way, e.g. by visual inspection of the sampling units in each set. For a reasonable choice of sampling procedure, only a global knowledge about the spatial distribution of herbage mass in the pasture is needed. Usually information on the use of the pasture in the past and of some soil characteristics is sufficient. From each experiment new information on the spatial distribution may become available, enabling (if necessary) improvements to be made in the sampling procedure.

2.5.1.4 *The size and shape of sampling units.* In general the shape of the sampling units of a given size has to be chosen in such a way that the variation in the population of sampling units is small. Practical limitations usually restrict the shape to a rectangle, ranging from a square to a very long and narrow strip. For many spatial distributions of the herbage mass, the best choice will be a long and narrow strip, placed at right angles to any trend in herbage mass.

Increasing the size of the sampling units, and choosing the shape to reduce edge effects within the practical limitations, will usually reduce the variability in the population of sampling units. When the total area sampled is constant, many small units will yield a more precise estimate of the herbage mass than a few larger ones, because the herbage mass at adjacent positions will be more alike than at distant positions. However small units require more organization and labour, with a higher cost, although laboratory costs can be reduced by combining the herbage for analysis from different small units. The best choice of shape and size therefore mainly depends on the particular local circumstances and possibilities.

The effect of the number of samples on the precision of the herbage mass estimates can be derived from the information in Section 2.5.1.3. The precision of the intake estimate is calculated as outlined in Section 2.5.2. If the sward method is to be applied for several years under the same circumstances it is advisable to carry out experiments so that information about the effect of the size of the sampling units on precision becomes available.

One method is to start with randomly chosen large pairs of units, subdivided into sections, in each of which the herbage mass is measured. On one unit of each pair, observations are obtained at the start, and on the other unit at the end of the grazing period. From these observations it is possible to estimate the standard errors of the estimates of herbage mass (at the beginning and end of the grazing period) and to estimate some spatial correlations. These observations also provide a better basis for choosing the sampling procedure. However, due to the variety of possible experimental designs and the complex statistical material produced it is advisable to consult a statistician during planning.

2.5.2 Estimation of intake

Two different ways of obtaining estimates of intake based on herbage mass are considered below, the procedures differing in the way the undisturbed accumulation is estimated:

System 1.  Cages are situated in the pasture in which the herbage mass is estimated, and measurement of the herbage mass in the cages is made at the end of the grazing period.

System 2.  In a separate paddock or in a fenced part of the area to be grazed, the herbage mass is estimated at the start as well as at the end of the grazing period.

The intake estimates are:

1. $\quad \hat{C}_1 = (\hat{Y}_s - \hat{Y}_e) + g^* (\hat{Y}_u - \hat{Y}_s)$ (2.12)

2. $\quad \hat{C}_2 = (\hat{Y}_s - \hat{Y}_e) + g^* (\hat{Y}_{u,e} - \hat{Y}_{u,s})$ (2.13)

where:

$\hat{Y}$ is the estimate for the herbage mass (index s for start, e for end, u for undisturbed) and g is the factor that describes the relation between disturbed and undisturbed accumulation (see Section 2.3). In system 2, $(\hat{Y}_{u,e} - \hat{Y}_{u,s})$ represents the increase in herbage mass in the separate grassland area. The standard error of the estimate of the intake $(\sigma_\wedge)$ for a given value of g is a function of the plot variances and correlations that can be derived by straightforward calculations.

If the units for the estimation of the differences in herbage mass $[(Y_s - Y_e)$ and $(Y_{u,e} - Y_{u,s})]$ are paired the standard error of $\hat{C}_2$ for a given value of g is:

$$\sigma_\wedge = \sqrt{[\sigma^2_{(Y_s - Y_e)} + g^2 \sigma^2_{(Y_{u,e} - Y_{u,s})}]}$$ (2.14)

However, g is not a constant according to Equation 2.5 and 2.7. Because in system 2 the undisturbed herbage accumulation is determined elsewhere, the correlations between $\hat{Y}_{u,e}$ or $\hat{Y}_{u,s}$, and $\hat{Y}_s$ or $\hat{Y}_e$ are zero. The other correlations affect the variance of the intake estimate and therefore it is worthwhile to choose the sampling units in such a way that the correlation between the estimates of the herbage masses are "optimal". Two such procedures are:

a.   all sampling units are randomly selected, so all correlations are zero;
b.   sampling units for estimating the herbage mass of the same pasture under different conditions are situated in pairs or triples.

The variance in the population of sampling units after grazing may be different from that in the population of sampling units before grazing. However, the advantage of adopting different numbers of units for estimating $Y_s$ and $Y_e$ is generally outweighed by the disadvantage of not pairing. How much the pairing reduces the variance of $\hat{C}$ depends on g, on the correlation between paired sampling units, and on the herbage mass estimates. Calculations on two years of experimental results by Meijs (1981) have shown that pairing reduced the number of samples needed to achieve the same precision by a factor 2.

Whether, in system 1 the cages should be placed near other units, depends on the correlations between the estimates concerned. Usually the size and shape of the cage units is not equal to the size and shape of the other units. This reduces the correlation between $\hat{Y}_u$ and $\hat{Y}_s$ and causes the variance of the cage units to be different from the variance of other units, making a different number of cage units compared with other units advantageous. It is generally advisable therefore not to group the 3 types of units. Because g is less than 1 and the standard error of $\hat{Y}_e$ is usually not much smaller than the standard error of $\hat{Y}_s$, in system 2 the total number of sampling units required is reduced when choosing relatively more pairs of sampling units in the pasture than in the exclosure.

The choice between systems 1 and 2 is often not obvious. When the shape of the cages is quite different from the shape of the other sampling units, system 2 will probably be more precise when using the same number of units on both systems, but there may be other situations in which system 1 is more precise. The choice between these systems is not a matter of precision alone. The cost and labour requirements may be larger when cages are used, and the importance of possible systematic errors must be considered. The possible bias caused by measuring the accumulation on a separate part of the pasture in system 2 has to balanced against the possible disturbance caused by the cages in the pasture using system 1.

### 2.5.3 Precision of herbage intake measurements

Some results on the precision of estimating herbage intake in grazing experiments have been summarised by Meijs (1981) and Meijs *et al.* (1982). Using 10 numbers of paired strips (motor scythe or sheep-shearing heads) the coefficient of variation of the mean intake was on average around 6% in pre-cut pastures. Results from a pre-grazed perennial ryegrass sward using an Agria motor scythe (8 paired strips) are shown in Figures 2.6 and 2.7 to illustrate the effect of the inclusion of double sampling (Lantinga, unpublished). For the sake of clarity, the amount of herbage accumulated during the grazing period was not included in the calculations. In this experiment, the stubble height of strips after cutting was measured in order to correct for possible differences in cutting height pre- and post-grazing. Height measurements were done with a tempex falling-plate meter (diameter 50 cm, pressure 1.7 kg m$^{-2}$). Per strip 10 meter readings were taken, whereas the number of height measurements in the pasture

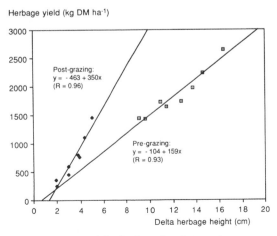

*Figure 2.6. Relationship between delta herbage height in strips as measured with a falling-plate meter, and herbage yield determined with an Agria motor scythe before grazing and after grazing under wet conditions.*

equalled 60 (systematic sampling). The weather conditions during this experiment were very wet. This caused trampling, reflected in an upward shift of the regression line between herbage height and herbage mass at the end of the grazing period (Figure 2.6). However, there was not a significant difference in cutting height before and after grazing (Table 2.4). This could be ascribed to the improvements made on handling the Agria motor scythe (see Section 2.2). The correlations between herbage removal in terms of height (corrected for stubble height differences) and mass are shown in Figure 2.7 for the eight paired strips. Based on the yield differences in the paired strips the calculated herbage intake was 1136 kg DM ha$^{-1}$. However, with the double sampling technique this figure was almost 20% lower (943 kg DM ha$^{-1}$). This was due to the observed differences in herbage height between the sampling units and pasture as a whole, pre-grazing as well as post-grazing. In the paired strips the average herbage removal was 9.1 cm, whereas in the pasture this was only 7.7 cm (Table 2.4).

The statistical analysis revealed that due to the inclusion of double sampling in this heterogeneous sward, there was a 20% improvement in the precision of the estimate of herbage intake in terms of s.e. (126 vs. 156 kg DM ha$^{-1}$). However, the main advantage of double sampling appeared to be a better description of the heterogeneity of the sward.

*Table 2.4. Mean herbage heights (cm) as measured with a falling-plate meter.*

|  | Pre-grazing | Post-grazing | Difference |
| --- | --- | --- | --- |
| Strips | 16.9 | 7.8 | 9.1 |
| Stubble | 4.6 | 4.4 | 0.2 |
| Pasture | 15.0 | 7.3 | 7.7 |

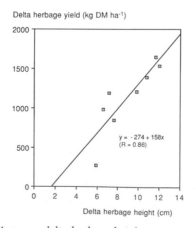

*Figure 2.7. Relationship between delta herbage height as measured with a falling-plate meter and delta herbage yield determined with an Agria motor scythe in paired strips before and after grazing under wet conditions.*

## 2.6 DIET SELECTION

It is often necessary in grazing trials to obtain information on the nutritive quality and botanical composition of herbage ingested by the grazing animal. Due to selection by the animal this will often differ from that of the herbage on offer and some attempt to assess dietary composition other than that based on herbage on offer is essential if relative differences between pastures in terms of animal production are to be interpreted critically.

### 2.6.1 Assessing the quality of grazed herbage

Two types of sward sampling methods are used:
1. Samples which represent the herbage grazed by the animals are obtained by cutting at "grazing height" or by hand-plucking. These samples are chemically analysed and the results are assumed to relate closely to the composition of the herbage eaten. The intensity of sampling depends on the heterogeneity of the pasture. For temperate improved pastures 8-20 samples per ha have been recommended (e.g. Brown, 1954). Samples are obtained immediately before or during grazing and one should attempt to sample vegetation that is typical of that being grazed. One method is to match the sample for analysis with that removed by the grazing animal after inspection of samples obtained before and after grazing (Cook, 1964; Kalmbacher and Washko, 1977).
   The above method is clearly subjective and liable to unknown bias (Chapter 3). For example, Langlands (1974) found that hand-plucking overestimated digestibility and N content in high quality pastures, and underestimated these components in low quality pastures when compared with samples obtained from oesophageally fistulated sheep. However, when a stratified sampling approach to hand-plucking is followed, diet digestibility can be closely predicted (Wallis de Vries, 1994). This refinement consists of sampling different plant categories separately (50-100 pickings for each category) and estimating diet digestibility according to the proportion of recorded bites on these categories using an observer computer program (Noldus, 1991). The samples have to be plucked between the thumb and a backward-bent forefinger, simulating the grazing process as good as possible. This method should prove especially valuable in heterogeneous and sparsely grazed vegetations, where animals can demonstrate a considerable selectivity. Moreover, hand-plucked samples are free from salivary contaminants that preclude reliable analyses for a number of parameters for nutritive quality in oesophageal extrusa or rumen samples (see Chapter 3). However, the method relies heavily on a calibration between operators and the study animal. In the experiments of Wallis de Vries (1994) the operator had been observing the grazing animals for at least two days before sampling.
2. Nutrient composition of grazed herbage is obtained indirectly by "difference". Samples cut before and after grazing to provide herbage mass data are used to provide sub-samples for chemical analysis or for determination of in-vitro digestibility. In case of system 2 for obtaining the estimate of intake (see Section

2.5.2) the quantity of each nutrient removed during grazing is calculated and expressed as a percentage of the OM removed as follows:

$$X = \frac{(N_s - N_e) + g * (N_{u,e} - N_{u,s})}{C}$$  (2.15)

where:

X is concentration of nutrient in herbage grazed (kg kg$^{-1}$ OM);

$N_s$ is amount of nutrient before grazing (kg ha$^{-1}$);

$N_e$ is amount of nutrient after grazing (kg ha$^{-1}$);

g is herbage accumulation factor (Equation 2.6);

$N_{u,e}$ is amount of nutrient after grazing in the undisturbed area (kg ha$^{-1}$);

$N_{u,s}$ is amount of nutrient before grazing in the undisturbed area (kg ha$^{-1}$);

C is amount of herbage consumed (kg OM ha$^{-1}$).

Provided that care is taken to obtain valid data for herbage mass, and samples are uncontaminated by soil and faeces, reasonably accurate data can be obtained. For example, Walters and Evans (1979) found that the coefficients of variation of estimates of digestibility of herbage grazed were only marginally higher by this method than by indirect animal techniques, and comparative digestibility estimates were in good agreement with those based on faecal nitrogen/digestibility regressions obtained in indoor feeding trials.

2.6.2 Assessing the botanical composition of grazed herbage

Sward sampling methods designed to assess the botanical composition of herbage grazed are similar in principle to those described for nutritive quality assessment. Thus two basic techniques can be identified:

1. Identifying and quantifying botanical components in samples purporting to represent grazed herbage. This technique, like that for quality assessment is subjective and liable to unknown bias. It cannot be recommended for many critical research studies, but can provide better guidance under some range or tropical conditions than indiscriminate sampling by cutting.
2. Identifying and quantifying by "difference" the botanical components removed by the grazing animal from samples cut to provide data on herbage mass before and after grazing, or also during grazing.

In both cases the techniques require that botanical components be expressed on a weight basis. Samples are analysed for botanical composition either directly by manual separation or by indirect methods as reviewed by Brown (1954) and 't Mannetje (1978) (see also Chapter 3).

A powerful tool to measure diet selection in mixed swards is the metallic frame described in Section 2.2.1.1. In an experiment for comparing the intake by steers of *Taraxacum* and grass, Neuteboom (unpublished) used the smallest sampling unit (the shaded area of 1.8 dm$^2$ in Figure 2.1). Samples were taken in patches of a strip with a relatively high dry weight proportion (about 35%) and in patches of a strip with a low proportion (about 5%) of *Taraxacum*. The mean dry weight proportion of *Taraxacum* in the whole paddock of 0.09 ha was 15%. The patches were chosen to be large enough to allow the cutting, in total, of 3 samples per patch at consecutive times (samples in triples). Measurements were done just before grazing (day 1, 4.30 pm) and twice during grazing (day 2, 9.30 am, and day 3, 9.00 am). During each harvest, 62 samples were cut in total (39 in the high and 23 in the low *Taraxacum* strip). In Figure 2.8 the time course of dry matter yields in both strips are shown, together with the grass and *Taraxacum* yields in the high *Taraxacum* strip. Although intake rates were low during the first part of the grazing period, it appeared that after the start of grazing the steers showed preference for *Taraxacum*. In the grass strip there was even a non-significant increase in dry matter yield. Between the three sampling events, total intake from *Taraxacum* in the high *Taraxacum* strip was significantly higher than from grass (0.69 ±0.10 vs. 0.43 ±0.08 kg DM per kg DM on offer, respectively). It is generally assumed that cattle like *Taraxacum* (e.g. Mott, 1955), but according to Müller (1966) the bitter tasting milky sap in the leaves and stems of *Taraxacum* would prevent the cattle from eating large quantities. The presented results indicate that patchwise high dry weight proportions in the order of 35% need not be a problem in pastures at all.

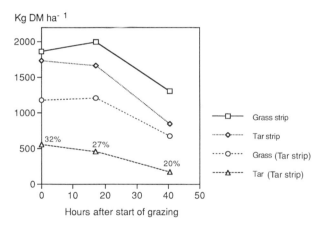

*Figure 2.8. Time course of dry matter yield in low Taraxacum patches (grass strip) and high Taraxacum patches (Tar strip) in a paddock grazed by steers. The percentages refer to the share of Taraxacum in the total dry matter yield of the Tar strip.*

To study diet selection in mixed swards, e.g. grass-white clover swards, relationships can also be established between the botanical composition of the sward and that of extrusa from oesophageally fistulated grazing animals. In a re-evaluation of data collected by Clark and Harris (1985) on mixed and strip grass-white clover swards grazed by sheep, Ridout and Robson (1991) used the concept of a selection coefficient (θ) instead of polynomials:

$$\theta = \left(\frac{Y}{100-Y}\right) / \left(\frac{X}{100-X}\right) \tag{2.16}$$

where Y is % clover in the diet as measured in extrusa and X is % clover in the sward as measured above sampling height (0.5 cm). This equation can be re-arranged to:

$$Y = \frac{100 \cdot \theta \cdot X}{100 + (\theta - 1) \cdot X} \qquad (2.17)$$

Using Equation 2.17 directly in a fitting procedure we obtained estimates of the selection coefficients and residual sum of squares (RSS) differing a little from those found by Ridout and Robson. They estimated $\log(\theta)$ as the mean of the log-transformed values following from Equation 2.16. In case of the mixed sward a fitted value of 2.10 was found for $\theta$, indicating an estimated selection ratio in favour of clover of about 2:1 (Figure 2.9).

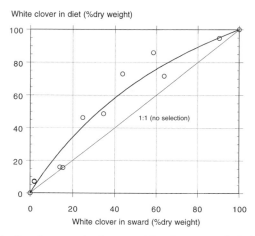

*Figure 2.9. Diet selection from a mixed grass-white clover sward. Relationship between dry weight in the sward and in the diet. Fitted curve is from Equation 2.17 with $\theta = 2.10$. (Recalculated from Ridout and Robson, 1991).*

## 2.7 REFERENCES

ALDER F.E. and MINSON D.J. (1963) The herbage intake of cattle grazing lucerne and cocksfoot pastures. *Journal of Agricultural Science, Cambridge*, **60**, 359-369.

BACK H.L., ALDER F.E. and GIBBS B.G. (1969) An evaluation of an electronic instrument for pasture yield determination. 2. Use with double sampling for regression estimation. *Journal of the British Grassland Society*, **24**, 168-172.

BIRCHAM J.S. and HODGSON J. (1983) The influence of sward condition on rates of herbage growth and senescence in mixed swards under continuous stocking management. *Grass and Forage Science*, **38**, 323-331.

BROUGHAM R.W. (1956). Effect of intensity of defoliation on regrowth of pasture. *Australian Journal of Agricultural Research*, **7**, 323-331.

BROWN Dorothy (1954) Methods of surveying and measuring vegetation. *Commonwealth Bureau of Pastures and Field Crops, Bulletin No. 42*, Farnham Royal: Commonwealth Agricultural Bureaux, 223 pp.

CARLIER L., PEETER A., LAMBERT J., BAERT J. and HENDRICKS C. (1989) Interet de l'herbometre dans l'evaluation du rendement de differents types de prairies. Comparison avec le capacimetre. *Herba*, **2**, 12-16.

CLARK D.A. and HARRIS P.S. (1985). Composition of the diet of sheep grazing swards of differing white clover content and spatial distribution. *New Zealand Journal of Agricultural Research*, **28**, 233-240.

COCHRAN W.G. (1977) *Sampling techniques*. New York: John Wiley & Sons.

COOK C.W. (1964) Symposium on nutrition of forages and pastures. Collecting forage samples representative of ingested material of grazing animals for nutritional studies. *Journal of Animal Science*, **23**, 265-270.

DAVIES Alison (1993) Tissue turnover in the sward. In: Davies Alison, Baker R.D., Grant Sheila A. and Laidlaw A.S. (eds.) *Sward Meaurement Handbook* (2nd edition), Reading: British Grassland Society, pp. 183-216

DAVIES D.A., FOTHERGILL M., DANIEL G.J. and MORGAN C.T. (1993) Animal production evaluation of herbage varieties. 2. Comparison of Aberystwyth S184, AberEndura and Grasslands Huia white clovers. *Grass and Forage Science*, **50**, 227-240.

DEENEN P.J.A.G. and E.A. LANTINGA E.A. (1993) Herbage and animal production responses to fertilizer nitrogen in perennial ryegrass swards. I. Continuous grazing and cutting. *Netherlands Journal of Agricultural Science*, **41**, 179-203.

FRAME J. (1993) Herbage mass. In: Davies Alison, Baker R.D., Grant Sheila A. and Laidlaw A.S. (eds.) *Sward Meaurement Handbook* (2nd edition), Reading: British Grassland Society, pp. 39-67.

GOUDRIAAN J. and MONTEITH J.L. (1990) A mathematical function for crop growth based on light interception and leaf area expansion. *Annals of Botany*, **66**, 695-701.

JONES R.J. and HAYDOCK K.P. (1970) Yield estimation of tropical and temperate pasture species using an electronic pasture measure. *Journal of Agricultural Science Cambridge*, **75**, 27-36.

KALMBACHER R.S. and WASHKO J.B. (1977) Time magnitude and quality estimates of forage consumed by deer in woodland clearways. *Agronomy Journal*, **69**, 497-501.

KING J., SIM E.M. and GRANT S.A. (1984) Photosynthetic rate and carbon balance of grazed ryegrass pastures. *Grass and Forage Science*, **39**, 81-92.

LANGLANWS J.P. (1974) Studies on nutritive value of the diet selected by grazing sheep. 7. A note on hand plucking as a technique for estimating dietary consumption. *Animal Production*, **19**, 249-252.

LANTINGA E.A. (1985a) Simulation of herbage production and herbage intake during a rotational grazing period: An evaluation of Linehan's formula. *Netherlands Journal of Agricultural Science*, **33**, 385-403.

LANTINGA E.A. (1985b) Productivity of grasslands under continuous and rotational grazing. *Doctoral Thesis. Agricultural University, Wageningen*, 111 pp.

LANTINGA E.A. (1988) Simulation of herbage production (In Dutch). *Gebundelde Verslagen* nr. 29, *Nederlandse Vereniging voor Weide- en Voederbouw, Wageningen*, pp. 32-38.

LEE M.R.F., JONES E. L., MOORBY J.M., HUMPHREYS M.O., THOEODOROU M. K., MACRAE J. C. and SCOLLAN N. D. (2001) Production responses from lambs grazing on Lolium perenne selected for an elevated water-soluble carbohydrate concentration. *Animal Research*, **50**, 441-449

LINEHAN P.A., LOWE J. and STEWART R.H. (1947) The output of pasture and its measurement. Part II. *Journal of the British Grassland Society*, **2**, 145-168.

McINTYRE G.A. (1978) Statistical aspects of vegetation sampling. In: Mannetje L. 't (ed.) Measurement of Grassland Vegetation and Animal Production. *Commonwealth Bureau of Pastures and Field Crops, Bulletin No. 52*, pp. 8-21, Farnham Royal: Commonwealth Agricultural Bureaux.

MANNETJE L. 't (1978) Measuring quantity of grassland vegatation. In: Mannetje L. 't (ed.) Measurement of Grassland Vegetation and Animal Production. *Commonwealth Bureau of Pastures and Field Crops, Bulletin No. 52*. Farnham Royal: Commonwealth Agricultural Bureaux, pp. 63-95.

MANNETJE L. 't (2000) Measuring Biomass of Grassland Vegetation. In: Mannetje L. t' and Jones R.M. (eds.) *Field and Laboratory Methods for Grassland and Animal Production Research*. CABI Publishing, Wallingford, UK. pp. 151-177.

MATCHES A.G. (1963) A cordless hedge trimmer for herbage sampling. *Agronomy Journal*, **55**, 309.

MEIJS J.A.C. (1981) Herbage intake by grazing dairy cows. *Agricultural Research Report 909*, Wageningen: Pudoc, 264 pp.

MEIJS J.A.C., WALTERS R.J.K. and KEEN A. (1982) Sward methods. In: Leaver J.D. (ed.) *Herbage Intake Handbook* (1st edition), Reading: British Grassland Society, pp. 11-36.

MICHELL P. (1982) Value of a rising plate meter for estimating herbage mass of grazed perennial ryegrass-white clover swards. *Grass and Forage Science*, **37**, 81-87.

MICHELL, P. and LARGE R.V. (1983) The estimation of herbage mass of perennial ryegrass swards: a comparative evaluation of a rising-plate meter and a single-probe capacitance meter calibrated at and above ground level. *Grass and Forage Science*, **38**, 295-299.

MOTT B. (1955) Ein Beitrag zur Festellung der Geschmackswertes der Grünlandpflanzen. *Das Grünland*, **4**, 31-40.

MÜLLER G. (1966) Ist der Löwenzahn auf Weiden ein Unkraut? *Landwirtschaftlichen Zeitschrift Nord Rheinprovinz*, 12.

NOLDUS L.P.J.J. (1991) The Observer: a software system for collection and analysis of observational data. *Behavior Research Methods, Instruments & Computers*, **23**, 415-429.

O'SULLIVAN M. O'KEEFEE W.F. and FLYNN M.J. (1987) The value of pasture height in the measurement of dry matter yield. *Irish Journal of Agricultural Research*, **26**, 63-68.

PARSONS A.J.. COLLETT B. and LEWIS J. (1984) Changes in the structure and physiology of a perennial ryegrass sward when released from a continuous stocking management: implications for the use of exclusion cages in continuous stocked swards. *Grass and Forage Science*, **39**, 1-9.

RIDOUT M.S. and ROBSON M.J. (1991) Diet composition of sheep grazing grass/white clover swards: a re-evaluation. *New Zealand Journal of Agricultural Research*, **34**, 89-93.

VAN ES A.J.H. (1978) Feed evaluation for ruminants. I. The system in use from May 1977 onwards in the Netherlands. *Livestock Production Science*, **5**, 331-345.

VICKERY P.J., BENNETT I.L. and NICOL G.R. (1980) An improved electronic capacitance meter for estimating herbage mass. *Grass and Forage Science*, **35**, 247-252.

WALLIS de VRIES M.F. (1994). Foraging in a landscape mosaic: Diet selection and performance of free-ranging cattle in heatland and riverine grassland. *Doctoral thesis. Agricultural University, Wageningen*, 161 pp.

WALTERS R.J.K. and EVANS E.M. (1979) Evaluation of a sward sampling technique for estimating herbage intake by grazing sheep. *Grass and Forage Science*, **34**, 37-44.

ZEMMELINK G. (1980) Effect of selective consumption on voluntary intake and digestibility of tropical forages. *Agricultural Research Reports 896*, Wageningen: Pudoc, 100 pp.

# CHAPTER 3

# ANIMAL-BASED TECHNIQUES FOR ESTIMATING HERBAGE INTAKE

**P.D. Penning**

## 3.1 INTRODUCTION

Estimating herbage intake by grazing animals is time consuming, labour intensive and relatively expensive. As advised in the first edition of this book (Greenhalgh, 1982) 'measurements of grazing intake should not be introduced into an experiment without giving the matter a good deal of thought'. One of the major questions that the experimenter should ask is, 'are the methods available likely to be successful in the particular circumstances of the experiment?'

Having started this chapter on a cautionary note, on the positive side it must be said that an understanding of ingestive behaviour of grazing animals can lead to an understanding of the grazing process that is difficult to achieve with alternative techniques. Amongst other things it has led to the development of practical management systems that enable maximisation of production per animal or output per unit area of land (Hodgson and Maxwell 1982; Parsons,1984). Although animal-based techniques require some interference with the grazing animals, they are potentially useable over a wide range of grazing circumstances and have been reviewed by Burns *et al.* (1994) and Coates and Penning (2000). Limitations and errors associated with these techniques have been discussed by Dumont and Iaason (2000). Three basic techniques have been developed (i) faeces output/diet digestibility, (ii) weighing animals and, (iii) energy expenditure, the latter is dealt with in Chapter 4.

Although the n-alkane method may be classified as a technique requiring faeces output/diet digestibility (i) it will be considered separately in this chapter because it overcomes some of the major problems associated with this method.

## 3.2 FAECAL OUTPUT AND DIET DIGESTIBILITY

The equation used to calculate intake (I) from estimates of faecal output (FO) and diet digestibility (D) is:

$$I = \frac{FO}{(1-D)} \qquad\qquad (3.1)$$

Estimation of I is therefore dependent upon accurate measurements of FO and D. It should be noted that error in estimating FO leads to an equivalent error in I. However, as D is usually > 0.5 and the complement of D (1-D) is used in the calculation, this leads to a proportionately greater error in estimates of I. For example, if D is estimated to be 0.8 with an error of estimate of 0.02 units this will give rise to an error in intake of 0.1 (0.02/(1-0.8)). Methods of estimating FO and D are described in the following two sections.

## 3.3 FAECAL OUTPUT

### 3.3.1 Total collection

Total faeces output can be measured by harnessing animals and fitting dung bags to collect all the faeces voided. The advantage of the total collection method is that it is relatively simple and few laboratory facilities are required. If dung is to be collected from female animals, urine separators may have to be used. However, White *et al.*, (1997) corrected faeces for urine contamination by measuring the ratio of N to ADF in samples of faeces collected directly from the animal's rectum. With female sheep it may be possible to use mesh bags, provided the faeces produced are relatively dry and pelleted.

Harnesses, dung bags and separators should be fitted to the animals several days before a collection period to accustom animals to wearing them, to allow adjustments in the harnesses to be made and to ensure that faeces are not being lost. Bottomless dung bags can be used for initial training, as they do not need regular emptying and can be fitted to the animals for several days at a time with minimum intervention by the experimenter.

The number of days over which faeces should be collected will vary according to experimental conditions. It is recommended that faeces should be collected for a minimum of 5 days, this being a compromise between the minimum length of time required to give a reasonable estimate of faeces production and to reflect the changes of digestibility and composition of the herbage being eaten. Continuous collection of faeces will give the best estimates of production but this is not usually practical.

3.3.1.1 *Equipment.* There are numerous designs for harness and dung bags. However, no particular type of harness appears to an have outstanding advantage. Detailed descriptions of harness have been given by Lesperance and Bohman (1961), Royal (1968), Cammell (1977) and Michell (1977). More recently, (M. J. Gibb personal communication) has modified and developed harnesses and collection bags for use with cows. These dung bags are manufactured by Flexitec Structures Ltd., 4 Mitchell Close, Segensworth, East Fareham, Hants PO15 5SE and are designed to retain both dung and urine.

3.3.1.2 *Sampling of faeces.* The frequency with which dung bags should be emptied is determined by the volume of faeces produced. Twice daily is generally recommended and is usually adequate for sheep. However, for dairy cows with high intakes and relatively low dry matter faeces, three or four times per day may be necessary.

Generally it is necessary to sub-sample the faeces produced daily because of the volume voided; after weighing and mixing thoroughly a daily aliquot sample is taken and these samples are stored frozen and bulked over the measurement period. Where faeces output is relatively low sub sampling may not be necessary.

3.3.1.3 *Processing of faeces samples.* For dry matter determination aliquot samples of faeces may be dried daily in a forced draught oven at 100°C and the dried samples bulked and mixed and sub-sampled again at the end of the faeces-collection period. Alternatively, the samples can be frozen, then allowed to thaw, thoroughly mixed and, if necessary, sub-samples taken for drying.

For drying, the samples are placed in solid-bottomed trays and dried at 100°C for 48 hours. Drying faeces at 100°C is not recommended if it is to be subject to subsequent chemical analyses other than for DM and ash, in this case freeze drying of the faeces should be carried out. It is recommended that N analysis is carried out on samples of fresh faeces where possible. After drying the faeces are milled and stored in sealed containers until analysed.

3.3.1.4 *Disadvantages of total collection.* The disadvantages of total collection of faeces are:

i.  Weighing and sub-sampling large volumes of faeces requires relatively high labour inputs. Approximate labour requirements are one person for 12 cows or 30 sheep (solely to look after harnesses, change dung bags and weigh, dry and sample faeces).

ii.   The animals' behaviour and performance may be affected by wearing harnesses and dung bags and the need to change the dung bags at frequent intervals may interfere with grazing patterns.

iii.  Collection from female animals is more difficult as it may be necessary to separate urine from faeces or to take extra faeces samples and increased chemical analyses, to correct for urine contamination.

iv.   Faeces may be lost from dung bags, giving underestimates of faeces production. Even when it is known that faeces collection is incomplete it is generally not possible to correct for this.

v.    Herbage growth, animal performance and animal behaviour may be affected by the prevention of the return of urine and faeces to the pasture.

3.3.2 Estimation of faeces production using markers (indicators)

The criteria for the ideal external marker to estimate faeces production were listed by Raymond and Minson (1955) as follows:

i.    It should be quantitatively recovered in the faeces (i.e. neither absorbed nor abnormally retained in the digestive tract). However, quantitative recovery is not always necessary and this will be discussed later in this chapter in the section dealing with the n-alkane technique (3.5).

ii.   It should be non-toxic.

iii.  It should be readily analysable by physical or chemical methods.

iv.   It should be present only in small amounts in the original diet.

It is recommended that faeces output (FO) be calculated as organic matter (OM), this corrects for the weight of marker dosed and soil ingestion influencing the weight of faeces produced. Using a marker, FO can be estimated using the following calculations:

$$\text{Faecal OM Output (g d}^{-1}) = \frac{\text{Weight of marker given (g d}^{-1}) \text{ x } \text{RR}}{\text{Mean concentration of marker in faeces OM (g g}^{-1}\text{OM)}} \qquad (3.2)$$

RR is the recovery rate of the marker and is:

$$\frac{\text{Total weight of marker excreted in faces (g)}}{\text{Total weight of marker given (g)}} \qquad (3.3)$$

RR is not generally measured within an experiment and is assumed to be 1.

A commonly used marker is chromic oxide ($Cr_2O_3$). This marker was first suggested by Edin (1918) and its use has been described in detail in a review of the use of markers in nutrition by Kotb and Luckey (1972). However, concerns have been expressed about the possible carcinogenic affects of handling $Cr_2O_3$ and its use is becoming less common, at least in the UK. The only commercially available product know to the author containing $Cr_2O_3$ is a controlled release device manufactured by

Captec NZ, P O Box 75340 Manurewa, Auckland NZ. The suppliers advise that they no longer manufacture this device but estimate that they have about 5 years supply in stock at the current rate of useage. Many other markers have been tried and have been reviewed by Kotb and Luckey (1972) and more recently Hatfield *et al.* (1990) and Peyraud (1998) used ytterbium; Bruckental *et al.* (1987) paraffin coated magnesium ferrite; Krysl *et al.* (1988) dysprosium and Mayes *et al.* (1995) titanium oxide. However, $TiO_2$ is normally present in the soil) and corrections for background levels of titanium in faeces need to be made. In fact titanium measured in faeces has been used to estimate soil ingestion by grazing animals (Healy, 1968).

3.3.2.1 *Carriers for markers.* Flow of markers through the digestive tract may be affected by the carrier used. Corbett *et al.* (1958; 1959) found that the flow of $Cr_2O_3$ through the duodenum was more regular when it was administered in impregnated paper than in gelatine capsules. Methods for the preparation of paper boluses containing $Cr_2O_3$ have been described by Troelsen (1963; 1966) and Moran and Gomez (1977).

Controlled release devices (CRDs) for $Cr_2O_3$ have been developed by Laby *et al.* (1984) and Furnvial *et al.* (1990) and their use has been reviewed by Parker *et al.* (1990). These intra-ruminal devices were designed to give a constant release rate of marker in the rumen for about 21 days. CRDs reduced fluctuations of marker concentration in the faeces and obviated the need for daily dosing. Hatfield *et al.*, (1991) compared CRDs with $Cr_2O_3$ dosed twice daily to estimate faeces production, they concluded that rate of release from the CRD was not always well controlled and this increased the variability in estimates of faecal production.

Markers can be included in the feed offered to dairy cows fed in parlour. Peyraud (1998) gave dairy cows 18g $Cr_2O_3$ per day divided between two meals by incorporation it into the concentrate at 5% of DM. Peyraud (1998) also used ytterbium oxide ($Yb_2O_3$) incorporated into the concentrate ration of dairy cows at 0.5% given in two meals per day resulting in a total intake of marker of 2g/cow/day. He found that $Yb_2O_3$ and $Cr_2O_3$ gave similar estimates of faeces production but animals consumed food containing the ytterbium more readily than that containing $Cr_2O_3$.

Chromium mordants have been successfully used (Van Soest, 1994) as a carrier for the marker. Chromium mordants can be prepared by boiling chopped dried herbage or straw for 1 h in a solution of sodium laurly sulphate (8g sodium laurly sulphate per litre; 25 l of solution per kg of straw). After rinsing the herbage is boiled for 24 h in a solution of sodium dichromate (15.7g sodium dichromate per l; 28 l solution per kg of straw) and then the absorbed dichromate is reduced to $Cr_2O_3$ with ascorbic acid (0.5 kg/kg straw). After this process the straw or herbage is oven dried 100°C and then milled (Uden *et al.*, 1980). It can then be measured into gelatine capsules or included in supplementary feed.

3.3.2.2 *Dosing and sampling frequencies.* Concentrations of marker in the faeces may show considerable diurnal fluctuations (Hardison and Reid, 1953) when administered in discrete doses. Patterns of dosing and sampling of faeces should be designed to minimise these fluctuations in marker excretion. In theory CRDs (see above) reduce fluctuation in marker concentrations.

A preliminary dosing period is required before sampling faeces for marker concentration. This allows the marker to equilibrate throughout the digestive tract. The time required for equilibration may vary with the marker used, the carrier used and levels of feed intake and rate of passage of digesta through the gut. In general practice a preliminary dosing period of 7 days is recommended followed by a 5 day measurement period. Chamberlain and Thomas (1983) and Melix et al., (1987) suggested that recovery of $Cr_2O_3$ could be considered to be 100% after an equilibration dosing period of 6 to 7 days.

An experimental routine that has been found to be satisfactory and practical is to dose animals twice per day, at 8 am and 5pm, and take samples of faeces directly from the rectum (grab samples) at the same times. The grab samples are bulked over the 5-day period oven dried at 100°C, ground and analysed for ash, and marker.

Raymond and Minson (1955) outlined a technique of sampling faeces from marked areas of pasture (ring sampling). These areas are cleared of faeces and then after a 24 h period faeces are collected from the rings. The size and number of the areas used will depend on the plot size and should be such that an adequate sample of faeces can be obtained for chemical analyses. If it is assumed that animals defecate at random, both spatially and temporally, then this method reduces problems associated with diurnal fluctuation in faeces marker concentrations. If this method is used in conjunction with CRDs (Parker et al., 1990) or with animals given the marker in supplementary feeds, then handling and interference with the animals is greatly reduced. However, this method only provides and estimate of group-mean intake of herbage. Coloured plastic particles can also be given to animals to identify the faeces of individuals on the pasture (Minson et al., 1960), however, this may require frequent dosing of the animals but, with cows fed supplements in the parlour, it may be included in their food.

3.3.2.3 *Pulse dosing.* Faecal marker concentration curves can be calculated *i.e.* plots of concentration of marker in faeces over time, following a single dose of a marker. Total faeces output can be calculated from these curves (France et al., 1988; Susmel et al., 1996). Currently, this technique requires frequent faeces samples to be taken to define the shape of the curve and thus it is not practical for grazing animals as frequent sampling severely interferes with patterns of grazing.

3.3.2.4 *Methods of minimising error and bias.* When a marker is used to estimate faeces production, the recovery rate is not normally checked within every experiment. However, when using a technique for the first time and periodically thereafter, it is advisable to carry out some or all of the checks listed below:

i.    Some animals on the experimental treatments should be fitted with harnesses and dung bags and the recovery rate of the marker checked. This is also recommended for CRDs as the release rate may vary from the specified rate (Furnival et al., 1990; Doyle et al., 1994; Coates and Penning, 2000). Faeces production may then be adjusted for recovery rate (Equations 3.2 and 3.3).

ii.   Some animals should not be dosed with the marker and their faeces analysed for the marker. This determines background levels of the marker so that recovery rates of marker can be adjusted for these levels. This is particularly important where pastures have been grazed by dosed animals over long periods.
iii.   Unbiased faecal outputs also depend on the recovery of the marker during chemical analysis. To check for this known concentrations of marker in faeces should be included in analytical runs (Costigan and Ellis, 1987).

3.3.2.5 *Accuracy of faeces output estimates.* Le Du and Penning (1982) calculated, from a literature review, that total faeces production using the $Cr_2O_3$ technique compared with measured faeces production was 96.1% (SD± 6.2). Peyraud (1998) reported that grab sampling increased variability of estimates by about 6% compared with sampling faeces from the pasture and Peyraud (1998); Melix *et al.,* (1987) found that using $Cr_2O_3$ increased variability in the estimation of faeces production by 4% to 7% compared with total collection. Chamberlain and Thomas (1983) compared the recovery rates of $Cr_2O_3$ administered in different carriers to dairy cows, they concluded that chromium mordanted straw had advantages compared with $Cr_2O_3$ administered as a powder or as impregnated paper and reported recovery of $Cr_2O_3$ of 0.941 (s.d., 0.022). Using CRDs Parker *et al.* (1990) estimated that with group sizes of 50 animals, differences in intake between groups of < 5% could be detected whilst Cruikshank *et al.* (1987) calculated that a 10% difference in mean intake could be detected at P<0.10 with group sizes of 6 animals using estimates of faeces output from dosed animals. However, because of its density and particle size $Cr_2O_3$ behaves as a heavy liquid when in water suspension (Van Soest, 1994) and tends to pass more rapidly from the rumen than fibre. Therefore, faeces estimation using markers relies on a relatively steady state in faeces production. Under non-steady state conditions estimation of faeces output using markers is inaccurate. This applies, for example, to rotational grazing where herbage mass, its botanical composition and digestibility are changing rapidly. Under these conditions the weighing technique is preferred (3.6)

3.3.3 Conclusions

When using total faeces collection, animals should be trained to carry the dung bags before experimental measurements are made and care should be taken that grazing is not affected by the technique being used. A recommended dosing period for markers is 12 days, comprising a preliminary dosing period of 7 days and faeces samples taken over the last 5 days, with twice-daily dosing regime, at approximately 8 and 16 hour intervals, with faeces samples taken at the same time. Using $Cr_2O_3$ a total daily doses of 0.5g to 1g and 5g to 10g is recommended for sheep and cattle, respectively, depending on size of the animal and their estimated intakes.

3.4 DIET DIGESTIBILITY

Digestibility of herbage consumed cannot be measured directly in grazing animals and therefore a number of indirect methods have been developed. The three major methods are: the ratio technique, the faecal index technique and *in vitro* digestibility; these techniques are described below.

3.4.1 The ratio technique

The digestibility of herbage can be estimated from the ratio of the concentration of an indigestible plant component (internal marker) in the feed ($i_h$) to that in the faeces ($i_f$):

Herbage intake (I g) x $i_h$ (g/g feed)=Faeces output (FO g) x $i_f$(g/g faeces)    (3.4)

Therefore the digestibility coefficient = $1 - \dfrac{i_h}{i_f}$                                        (3.5)

This technique requires (1) that the marker be unaltered in its passage through the animal, (2) that it can be quantitatively recovered and (3) that feed and faeces are accurately sampled.

Internal markers have been reviewed by Van Soest (1994) and some of the major plant components that have been suggested as markers are lignin, chromogen, silica, acid insoluble ash, plant waxes (this will be covered separately in section 3.5 dealing with n-alkanes) and indigestible fibre components of feed and faeces. Penning and Johnson (1983a) investigated the use of potentially indigestible cellulose (PIC) and acid insoluble ash (AIA) as markers. They concluded that AIA could not be recommended and that, although PIC predicted digestibility well, the technique was impractical for use on a large scale. Penning and Johnson (1983b) investigated the use of indigestible acid detergent fibre (IADF) as an internal marker. They concluded that IADF predicted digestibility well but the relationship between digestibility, calculated using IADF with digestibility measured *in vivo,* was non linear and that further work to develop this technique was required.

Lignin has been found to work reasonably well in herbage with a high lignin content for example the error in estimating digestibility is about 10% at 4% lignin in the diet and about 20% at 2% lignin in the diet (Van Soest, 1994). However, in general no internal marker has been found to be entirely successful, for example neither chromogen nor liginin are specific entities and material analysed in the feed may differ from that in the faeces. As a result, markers such as lignin and IADF may give variable results (Dove and Coombe, 1992).

3.4.2 The faecal index technique

This method requires a conventional indoor *in vivo* digestibility trial to be undertaken with herbage similar to that being grazed, and that the faecal component is related to the *in vivo* digestibility; this compound need not be indigestible. The concentration of this component is then measured in faecal samples from grazing animals taking into account any diurnal patterns in its excretion.

Nitrogen is the faecal component most frequently used (Chenost, 1985; Holecheck *et al.*, 1986) and the technique is at its best when local regressions are produced for each specific set of circumstances, as relationships between faecal N and digestibility are not constant and vary with herbage species, season, locality and fertiliser treatment of the pasture (Coates and Penning, 2000). Harvesting of herbage, for the *in vivo* digestibility trial that is representative of the herbage selected by the grazing animals, is a major difficulty and a digestibility trial running in parallel with the grazing experiment is required, with its attendant labour and facility requirements. In some cases sheep have been used in the digestibility trials, to reduce the work load, and the N regressions calculated applied to grazing cattle. This method is questionable since differences in efficiency of digestion between species have been reported (Blaxter *et al.,* 1966; Playne, 1978). The usefulness of the technique is therefore restricted to situations in which herbage similar to that being grazed can be harvested for a digestibility trial. The technique may be difficult to use in continuous stocking experiments or where animals have the ability to select between plant species or plant components.

However, Peyraud (1998) reviewed the use of the N technique and concluded that the method gives satisfactory accuracy (RSD 0.015 - 0.020, Greenhalgh and Corbett, 1960; Barthiaux-Thill and Oger, 1986; Comeron and Peyraud, 1993). Nevertheless, the slopes of the linear and curvilinear equations calculated by these workers differed and the use of locally derived regressions was recommended. Peyraud (1998) pointed out that the faccal N content ($N_f$, %OM) is of endogenous and microbial origin and is a good marker of digestibility (D) because it varies in a passive way with the cell wall content of the faeces. Using 1208 graminaceous grassland plants Demarquilly and Jarrige (1981) found that the content of apparently indigestible nitrogen present ($N_u$, %OM) is linearly related to the N content of herbage ($N_h$, %OM):

$$N_u = 0.637 + 0.069 N_h \qquad\qquad (3.6)$$

The amount of N excreted by animals ($qN_f$) can be expressed as:

$qN_f = (0.637 + 0.069 N_h) \times \text{Intake}(I)$ As $qN_f = I \times (1\text{-}D) \times N_f$ then using these equations:

$$D = 1 - (0.069 N_h + 0.637)/N_f \qquad\qquad (3.7)$$

This relationship can be treated as a series of linear or quadratic segments which account for the wide diversity of N regression models reported and their relatively restricted range of validity (Peyraud, 1998).

For a given $N_f$, digestibility of herbage tends to be lower in autumn and in legumes compared with spring grass (Comeron and Peyraud, 1993). By pooling the results from cattle given perennial ryegrass, cocksfoot and herbage from permanent pastures (Greenhalgh *et al.,* 1960; 1966a and b; Barthiaux-Thill and Oger, 1986; Comeron and Peyruad, 1993), Peyruad (1998) calculated the following equation:

$$D = 0.975 - 0.633/N_f \quad (r^2 = 0.85, \text{RSD} = 0.017, D = 0.70\text{-}0.86) \qquad\qquad (3.8)$$

Peyruad (1998) pointed out that the coefficients in equation (3.8) were similar to those obtained for tropical grasses with much lower digestibilities (Boval *et al.,* 1996) and therefore it is possible to generate equations of a general nature.

The combined use of several predictors can improve the accuracy of prediction, for example, for a population of perennial ryegrass, cocksfoot, white clover and mixed swards the precision of the prediction of D based on $N_f$ alone was RSD 0.020. This was improved to 0.013 by the inclusion Acid Detergent Fibre content of the faeces ($ADF_f$, %OM) (Peyruad, 1998). Comeron and Peyraud (1993) calculated the following equation to predict D:

$$D = 0.791 + 0.0.334 N_f - 0.0038\ ADF_f \tag{3.9}$$

This equation has been routinely used in grazing experiments by Delagarde *et al.* (1999) and Peyraud *et al.* (1998).

If satisfactory relationships can be calculated for the faecal index technique that cover the range of herbage digestibilities found under the grazing conditions being examined, this obviates the need to sample herbage grazed to estimate its digestibility and overcomes the difficulties associated with diet selection by the animals, indeed, it may be used to estimate differences in herbage digestibilities between individual animals.

3.4.2.1 *Derivation of N regressions.* To calculate N regressions it is necessary to run a standard digestibility trial (Schneider and Flatt, 1975; Burns *et al.,* 1994) feeding fresh grass similar to that being grazed. The measurements required are: feed intake and faeces output (DM), ash content of feed and faeces and faecal N, ADF etc.

Greenhalgh *et al.* (1960) demonstrated that using three animals and sub-periods of three days, the standard error of prediction should not be greater that 1.0 unit of digestibility: this may be slightly reduced if longer periods are used. However, if the digestibility of the herbage is changing rapidly with time, sub-periods should be kept as short as is practical.

Animals used in a digestibility trial should be housed in individual pens and offered herbage at a level of intake close to that of their grazing contemporaries. Equipment to enable total collection of faeces voided is required for each animal.

Animals should be introduced to their digestibility stalls and offered fresh grass at least one week before the trials begin so that they can become accustomed to their feed, surroundings and the equipment being used. This initial period also enables voluntary intake to be estimated and, once this has been established, the level of herbage offered should be set at 90% of voluntary intake, so that all feed is consumed and diet selection avoided.

Steps should be taken to minimise deterioration of the herbage between cutting and its being eaten by the animals. At least two feeds per day are required and in some cases more when intakes are high. Weather conditions will also influence the cutting and feeding frequencies necessary; in hot or humid conditions it may be necessary to cut herbage twice daily or to cold store it to minimise fermentation and heating of the material.

A fixed level of herbage intake should be maintained for at least four days before the commencement of faecal collection, in order to achieve a steady state of faecal and N output. A standard quantity of herbage DM should be offered daily, this requires some method for the rapid determination of dry matter in the fresh herbage. Microwave ovens have been successfully used (Schild and Honig, 1975) but they should be fitted with a dummy load ( a separate container of water is suitable), to prevent damage to the magnetron when all the moisture from the grass has been removed. An alternative is to heat the herbage in oil (Brown and Duval, 1907; Cammell, 1977).

Depending on the type of animal used, level of intake and method of faeces collection, faeces need to be removed 1-3 times per day; one of these occasions should coincide with collecting any feed refusals and the offering of a new day's feed. The weights of any refusals, herbage offered and faeces produced should be weighed and two sub samples taken, one for dry matter determination and an aliquot sample for chemicals analyses. Samples for chemical analyses should be rapidly frozen and cold stored. At the end of each measurement period aliquot samples should be thawed, mixed and sub sampled and analysed for DM, ash and N. N analyses should be carried out on fresh material where possible. If this is not possible then faeces from the digestibility and grazing trial must be dried by the same method and N contents determined in the dry material.

The N regression from the digestibility trial is the calculated as digestibility (%, y) against N% of faeces (x) (see earlier in this section, alternative non-linear equations). The equation derived is then used to predict the digestibility of the diet selected by the grazing animals, this is best expressed on an organic matter basis, to remove effects of soil ingestion by the animals.

When applying the equation in grazing studies samples of faeces should be taken from individual animals. These can be sub samples from total faeces collection or collected as grab samples. For the latter, it may be necessary to correct for diurnal variation in N concentration, but it is generally considered that faecal N concentration varies little throughout the day.

Grazing animals generally have a higher intake than housed animals; Minson and Raymond (1958) found that diet digestibility decreased by 1.5% units when intake was increased by 50% although a decrease of only 0.7% was predicted from the N regression technique. Similarly, Valderrabano (1979) reported that when intake was increased from maintenance to twice maintenance, digestibility fell by 3% units whilst a fall of only 0.7% units was predicted from the N regression. Therefore, N regressions may over-estimate the digestibility of diets selected by grazing animals.

3.4.2.2 *Cutting and preparing the forage.* When harvesting forage for a digestibility trial, material as similar as possible to that being grazed is required. In particular, height of cut must be carefully considered since this can have a major influence on the proportion of leaf, stem and dead material harvested and thus on digestibility of the herbage. For sheep trials it is possible to use a reciprocating-blade mower and then to collect the herbage manually (Penning and Gibb, 1979). For cattle, a drum mower followed by a forage wagon with a pick-up reel is recommended. The objective should be to minimise physical damage to the herbage being harvested. The use of forage harvesters that chop and lacerate the herbage are not recommended as damage to the herbage may lead to its rapid heating and influence its intake and digestibility.

Once the herbage has been harvested a representative sample should be taken and its dry matter determined using one of the rapid drying methods given in 3.4.2.1 above. This enables a constant amount of dry matter to be offered to animals daily and overcomes weight differences due to variation in water content of the herbage.

### 3.4.3 In vitro digestibility procedures.

Laboratory procedures have been reviewed in detail by Jones and Moseley (1993),Van Soest (1994) and Weiss (1994). The two main methods used are the two-stage *in vitro* procedures using rumen liquor (Tilley and Terry, 1963) and the enzymatic technique (Jones and Hayward, 1975) and these will be described below. In addition, the *in sacco technique* and Near Infra Red Spectral Analysis (NIRS) techniques will be briefly considered.

3.4.3.1 *Two stage in vitro method.* The Tilley and Terry (1963) method consists of incubating a small amount of feed (0.5g) in rumen fluid. After fermentation for 48 h the residue is digested with acid-pepsin. There have been many modifications to this technique for example, Alexander and McGowan (1966); Minson and McLeod (1972). These modifications enable laboratory throughputs of 200 - 300 samples a week to be achieved. Variation in sample analysis caused by analytical technique can be controlled relatively easily, however, the major cause of poor precision is variation in the activity of rumen liquor used (Barnes, 1967). The effects of diet, time of sampling and species of donor animal etc. can all have major effects on the activity of the inoculum and these factors have been reviewed in detail by Weiss (1994). A major drawback of this technique is the requirement to maintain rumen fistulated animals as donors but to overcome this El Shaer *et al.* (1987), used fresh sheep faeces as the inoculum source. Subsequent testing found that using inoculum prepared from faeces gave similar results (Table 1) to rumen liquor (Omed *et al., 1989*).

Different equations have been calculated to predict *in vivo* from *in vitro* digestibility and no general relationship seems to exist. Weiss (1994) reported intercepts of linear regressions (OMD% *in vivo* = a + b *in vitro* digestibility%) varied from 0.4 to 17 and the slopes varied from 0.7 to 1.3. It is recommended that samples of herbage of known *in vivo* digestibility (standards) are included in any analytical run and these are used to correct *in vitro* values. These standards should have digestibility values close to those expected for the herbage being grazed, should be derived from similar herbage and at the same level of intake, as that achieved by the grazing animals. Standards and samples of grazed herbage should be dried in the same manner.

3.4.3.2 *Enzymatic methods.* These have been reviewed by extensively by Weiss (1994) and Van Zoest (1994) and will only be covered briefly here. One of the first reported enzymatic methods reported was that used by Donefer *at al.* (1963).

*Table 3.1. Linear regressions of* in vivo *(y) upon* in vitro *(x) digestibility (%) using different methods to estimate in vitro digestibility (Omed et al., 1989).*

| Method | Rumen liquor-pepsin | | | Faeces liquor-pepsin | | | Pepsin-cellulase | | |
|---|---|---|---|---|---|---|---|---|---|
| Herbage | Intercept | Slope | RSD | Intercept | Slope | RSD | Intercept | Slope | RSD |
| Grasses | -13.56 | 1.20 | 1.85 | -3.95 | 1.07 | 2.28 | 25.06 | 0.76 | 2.03 |
| Lucerne | -0.98 | 1.03 | 1.94 | 2.78 | 0.95 | 0.61 | -8.22 | 1.07 | 1.58 |
| Grasses +Lucerne | -4.82 | 1.08 | 1.93 | -2.78 | 1.05 | 1.75 | 10.47 | 0.90 | 7.73 |
| All Grasses[1] | 0.52 | 1.01 | 1.46 | - | - | - | 34.72 | 0.56 | 1.80 |
| All Legumes[1] | -1.86 | 1.04 | 1.91 | - | - | - | 6.94 | 0.87 | 3.17 |

[1] Data from Terry *et al.* (1978).

Jones and Hayward (1973;1975) amongst others developed the technique further. Briefly, samples are incubated in a mixture of HCl (0.1N) and pepsin (0.2% w/v) for 24 h at 40°C to 50°C. The pepsin solution is removed and cellulase solution added and the samples incubated for a further 24 to 48 h. Digestibilities vary with the source of cellulase used and are often lower than those measured *in vivo.* For greater detail on these effects the readers are referred to the review by Weiss (1994).

Because of many factors affecting the relationship between *in vivo* digestibility and digestibility estimated using enzymes, it is recommended that local regression equations be established. As with the *in vitro* technique, a sample set of known *in vivo* digestibility should be included in any analytical run so that values can be corrected for bias. Weiss (1994) reported that the RSD for all results of the pepsin HCl-cellulase technique varied between 2 to 4% units. It is suggested that if predicted values differ from actual values by more than 4% units then the results should be discarded. Table 1 shows comparisons of OMD estimated using the *in vitro* technique, using both rumen-liquor and faeces-liquor as the inoculum source, with the enzymatic technique. Generally, for the pepsin-cellulase technique, regression coefficients are less than 1 and RSDs are greater than for the other methods.

3.4.3.3 *In sacco technique.* This technique involves placing samples of herbage in bags made from materials that are not digested by enzymes in the rumen. The bags containing the samples are placed into the rumen of cannualted animals and then left for a period of time and DM or OM disappearance measured. Excellent reviews of this technique have been made by Nocek, 1988 and Weiss, 1994. Very few data have been published comparing *in sacco* with *in vivo* digestibility and it should be pointed out that the *in sacco* technique usually only measures events that occur in the rumen whilst *in vivo* digestibility is digestion over the whole digestive tract. DM disappearance *in sacco* is generally related to *in vivo* digestibility but, because of large numerical differences, *in sacco* technique cannot be recommended to estimate *in vivo* digestibility (Weiss, 1994).

3.4.3.4 *Near Infra Red Spectral (NIRS) analysis.* Lyons and Stuth (1992) developed calibration equations for predicting OMD level in the diet from free ranging cattle from NIR analysis of faeces and also for OMD of the diet of free ranging goats (Leite and Stuth, 1995). This technique requires the development of calibration sets of data, where samples of faeces from animals consuming a diet of known digestibility, similar to that available to grazing animals are used. This is similar to methods used to develop N regressions (3.4.2.1) but sophisticated software supplied with commercially available NIRS equipment enables the data to be manipulated, analysed and the spectra to be stored. For further information on NIRS techniques the readers are referred to reviews by Murray (1993) and Givens and Deaville (1999).

3.4.4 The collection of samples of herbage being grazed

Collection of samples representative of the herbage being grazed is essential for the successful use of *in vitro* techniques. However, the collection of these samples is difficult.

There are two basic methods for sample collection:

i.    Manual - snip or pluck samples taken from the sward by the experimenter following close observation of the grazing animal.
ii.   Animal - by surgically prepared animals, fistulated at the oesophagus or the rumen.

Both methods require that the samples are collected at a number of points through the grazing period to measure any changes in digestibility that may occur.

The number and distribution of samples required will depend on changes in herbage state over the grazing cycle. If the herbage on offer is homogenous and changes little over the grazing period (for example on continuously stocked monocultures maintained at a constant sward surface height) then the number of samples taken need only be sufficient to account for random variation and the degree of precision required. For mixed swards, including legumes, herbs, shrubs and trees, the requirement for sampling will be more complex, particularly when diet preference and selection changes with time of day. Not only must samples taken be representative of the diet selected by the animals but, the proportion of each herbage component in the sample, should be similar to that in the diet selected by the grazing animal.

An example of changes in sward composition and intake rate by sheep on a rotationally grazed ryegrass pasture is given in Figure 3.1. To enable these measurements to be made the sward was grazed down relatively slowly, but these results could be extrapolated to a sward that is stocked at a higher rate in which herbage is depleted rapidly. Initially, animals have a very high intake rate and are eating mainly live lamina, as lamina is removed pseudo stem is consumed and also some dead herbage, leading to low intake rates. Intake rate decreases in a non-linear manner and thus as each component of the sward has a different digestibility it is difficult to sample the herbage in such a way to enable mean diet digestibility to be estimated. Similar results for dairy cows have been presented by Barrett *et al.* (2001).

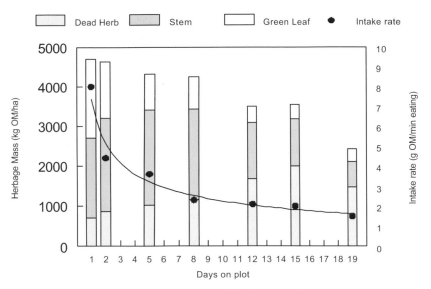

*Figure 3.1. Changes in sward composition and herbage intake rate on a ryegrass sward rotationally grazed by lactating ewes (Penning et al.,1994).*

This example demonstrates the thought that must be put into the various methods of herbage sampling and shows how the technique chosen to estimate intake will have to be adapted to meet experimental conditions.

3.4.4.1 *Manual Collection.* This technique depends on the experimenter carefully observing what plants and parts of plants the grazers are eating and then mimicking this selection by either hand plucking or snipping, with scissors or hand-held shears, similar herbage. Samples of material collected should be in the same proportion as those selected by the animals (but see n-alkane technique in this chapter). Where diet preference and selection change over the day, sampling programmes must be devised not only to account for these diurnal patterns but also to changes in diet, in the longer term, associated with increase or depletion of biomass on offer to the animals. A modification to the plucking technique for use under grazing conditions where sward height is being rapidly reduced has been described by Peyraud (1998). Bunches of tillers are cut to ground level before grazing commences and the samples frozen. After grazing, residual tiller height is measured and the frozen tillers are cut at the residual sward height of the grazed pasture and this portion of the sample is used for chemical analysis. Under conditions where there is little scope for the animal to select, manual techniques work well but are more problematic when animals are able to select from a range of herbage species.

Once collected, the herbage samples should be rapidly frozen to prevent deterioration and stored frozen to await drying, processing and analysis.

3.4.4.2 *Collection of samples from fistulated animals.* Techniques for the collection of samples of grazed herbage by animals fistulated either at the rumen (Tayler and Deriaz, 1963) or oesophagus (Torell, 1954; Hamilton *et al.,* 1960) have been developed. However, the use of oesophageally fistulated animals (OFs) has superseded the use of rumen fistulated animals and subsequent discussion will be centred on the use of OFs for the collection of samples of herbage. Description of the surgical techniques for the preparation of fistulae are beyond the scope of this book but are described in papers by Torell (1954) and Hamilton *et al.* (1960).

Legal requirements and ethical considerations govern the use of surgically-prepared animals in many countries and these aspects must be taken into account when designing experiments. In the United Kingdom all animal experiments are subject to the Animals (Scientific Procedures) Act 1986 and require that a cost benefit analysis be employed to balance ethical considerations against likely benefits to arise from the experiment.

The major scientific argument put forward for the use of fistulated animals is that they overcome the major problems associated with subjective selection used in manual collection of herbage samples (Van Dyne and Torell, 1964). Although using OFs may overcome these problems of selection, it is essential to be certain that samples, after their inevitable mastication and addition of saliva, do not introduce some other bias into the subsequent analysis.

It has been shown that extrusa samples may not be representative of the diet of the resident animals on the experiment (Coates *et al.,* 1987; Jones and Lascano, 1992; Clements *et al.,* 1996). These differences may arise from differences in diet preference and selection between OFs and intact animals or due to herbage samples from OFs being collected over a relatively short period differing from that consumed over the whole day. Coates *et al.* (1987) demonstrated how diet preference may change over the day and Parsons *et al.* (1994) showed how previous history and fasting (Newman *et al.,* 1994) affected preference and diet selection.

3.4.4.3 *Experimental design.* In the past cross over designs and the introduction of fistulated animals to the grazed paddocks for short periods have been used. In view of the problems identified in 3.4.4.2 these methods should be used with caution. In addition, Baldock (1985) showed that the introduction of sheep into a new flock or the mixing of flocks was extremely stressful and affected behaviour. It is therefore recommended that OFs are kept with other animals on the test area throughout any experiment, not only will this enable them to be accustomed to the diet but will also enable social bonds to develop (Lynch *et al.,* 1992). This should also improve the chances of obtaining a herbage sample representative of what the main body of animals is consuming.

3.4.4.4 *Working with fistulated animals.* The objective is to obtain a sample of herbage representative of that grazed by the main body of animals. The chances of obtaining samples of herbage are better if the times of collection coincide with normal bouts of grazing activity.

The collection of samples requires that the animal be restrained and its plug removed, extraneous material should be cleared from around the fistula, a throat plug may be fitted to increase recovery rate of extrusa, a plastic bag attached around the neck of the animal and it is then allowed to graze. Animals should be trained to tolerate both throat plugs (see Chapter 6) and the collection bag before sample collection is attempted. Care must be taken that the animal is not ruminating when the plug is removed or regurgitated material will enter the sampling bag. If rumination takes place during the sampling period or if water or any other materials (other than the herbage to be sampled) is consumed, the sample should be discarded. After sampling the animal is again restrained, the sample bag removed and the fistula plug re-inserted. The duration of the sampling period will depend on the weight of sample required and the intake rate of the herbage. In general, the plug should not remain out of the fistula for more than 30 min to prevent excessive loss of saliva and to avoid the fistula shrinking making the re-insertion of the fistula plug difficult. When herbage mass is high, samples can be collected in a few minutes but, when it is low, animals may be reluctant to graze and collection of an adequate sample may be difficult.

Inherent in the collection of samples using OFs is that the herbage will be contaminated with saliva. The quantity of saliva added to a sample will vary between animals and will also vary with the rate of consumption of the herbage. The saliva cannot be removed from the sample without taking some of the soluble plant components with it and thereby reducing the digestibility of the whole sample. If saliva is left in the sample, the sample will be contaminated with salivary salts, N and organic matter. Even if digestibility is expressed on an organic matter basis, an over estimate will occur because salivary organic matter is completely digestible. The degree of under or over estimation can be in the order of 3-4 and 1-2 units, respectively (Langlands, 1966). Gonzales and Lambourne (1966) reported increases in *in vitro* digestibility of up to 4.2 percentage units due to the addition of saliva.

Table 3.2 shows some effects of the addition of saliva to fresh herbage cut and fed to sheep at two levels of feeding (Valderrabano, 1979). There was little effect on digestibility of herbage for animals fed at maintenance but for herbage offered *ad libitum* differences were found, in addition RSDs tended to be higher for extrusa than herbage. Langlands (1967) concluded that samples containing a large amount of saliva should be discarded.

*Table 3.2. Effects of feeding level and addition of saliva on relationships between* in vivo *(y) and* in vitro *(x) digestibility by sheep of fresh herbage (y= a + bx) (Valderrabano, 1979).*

| Material | Feeding level | a | b | RSD ± |
|----------|---------------|------|-------|-------|
| Fresh Grass | Maintenance | 0 | 1.061 | 2.02 |
| Extrusa | Maintenance | 0 | 1.007 | 3.14 |
| Fresh Grass | *Ad libitum* | 18.52 | 0.804 | 2.85 |
| Extrusa | *Ad libitum* | -9.39 | 1.130 | 3.21 |

As soon as the sample has been collected it should be sealed in an air-tight bag and instantly frozen in dry ice (solid $CO_2$). Delays in freezing can result in losses of dry matter due to continued plant respiration and fermentation, potentially leading to a depression in estimated digestibility.

3.4.4.5 *Processing the extrusa samples.* All samples for chemical analysis should be freeze-dried rather than oven-dried, to minimise the loss and denaturing of chemical components. The entire sample should be dried and then ground to pass through a fine sieve (e.g. 0.8 mm) and any sub-sampling should be on the dried and ground material, as it is difficult to sub-sample frozen extrusa since the solid and liquid phases tend to freeze as separate fractions. Freeze drying leaves a sample containing approximately 90% DM and correction of all subsequent analytical results to 100% DM should be carried out. This correction factor is best derived by oven drying a separate sub sample of the freeze dried material at 100°C for 4 hours or by determining a chemical dry matter using the Karl Fischer (Fischer,1935) technique.

Fine grinding of the samples is necessary to facilitate good mixing and to allow representative sub-samples to be taken for analysis, particularly as most chemical analyses are carried out on samples of 0.5 g or less. Fine grinding is also important for the proper functioning of the *in vitro* technique. Particles of coarsely-ground forage can float to the top of the digestion tubes and may not be completely digested, thus biasing the estimation of digestibility.

### 3.4.5 Interpretation and use of *in vitro* digestibility data

Whilst the various techniques described can be used to estimate *in vivo* digestibility of forage, the estimates are almost exclusively related to *in vivo* determinations made using whether sheep offered dried herbage at a maintenance level of feeding. This base line is satisfactory e.g. in ranking grass species in plant breeding trials or for ranking quality of conserved forages. However, when a derived digestibility is used together with an estimate of faecal production to estimate herbage intake, other factors have to be taken into account. Amongst these are differences between animal species, effects of level of intake and the effects of other feeds on herbage digestibility

3.4.5.1 *Level of intake.* It is well recognised that in ruminants, as intake of a feed increases so its digestibility is reduced. This gives rise to different relationships between *in vivo* and *in vitro* digestibility (Table 3.2).

This reduction in digestibility is not related to any quantifiable characteristics of the herbage and therefore no rational correction can be made. Neither can a correction be made until intake has been measured and the level of feeding above maintenance established.

For animals offered herbage *ad libitum* the effects of level of intake can be quite large and this may have a large effect on the estimation of intake. It has been proposed that a reduction of 1.5 percentage units of digestibility be applied to digestibility *in vitro* when this value is used to calculate intake by grazing animals (Commonwealth Agricultural Bureau, 1961). However, these problems can be overcome, to some extent, if values of *in vitro* digestibility are corrected using appropriate sets of standards (3.4.3.1).

Langlands and Bennett (1973) used the equation given by Blaxter (1961) to correct the estimated intake by grazing sheep. Wilkins (1969) suggested a method for correcting for level of intake by using potentially digestible cellulose in feed and faeces. Wilkins (1969) suggested that this technique would allow intake to be calculated without relying on the relationship between *in vivo* and *in vitro* digestibility. Essentially, this technique is the same as using an internal marker (3.4.1) in this case the marker being indigestible cellulose.

3.4.5.2 *Associative effects of dietary ingredients.* When two or more feeds are offered, the digestion of one is not independent of the other and offering supplements to grazing animals may give rise to changes in ingestive behaviour that cannot be measured indoors Milne and Mayes (1986). The degree to which one feed interacts with another depends on their relative compositions. For example, when a cereal is offered with forage, the availability of rapidly fermentable carbohydrate in the cereal will modify the rumen fermentation pattern ( Delegarde *et al.*, 1999). Also feeding N supplements may increase the intake of herbage with a low N content (Delegarde *et al.,* 1999), whilst feeding cereal supplements may decrease grazing time, herbage intake and affect diet digestibility (Penning *et al.,* 1988). In grazing experiments it is, therefore, unreasonable to apply digestibility coefficients derived from herbage when fed alone to herbage that is offered as part of a more complex diet. One procedure that has been used in indoor experiments is to feed various ratios of the components of the complex diet and to calculate the digestibility of each component using simultaneous equations (Kromann, 1973). This method cannot be used at pasture since the quantity of grass consumed is unknown. However, it may be used to assess the likely magnitude of effects but cutting grass and feeding it indoors. A method of extrapolating the results of an indoor experiment to account for associative effects under grazing has been described by Milne *et al.* (1981).

A solution for a two component diet at pasture, where the intake of one component is known my be calculated by using markers. If we use a grass/cereal diet as an example:

$$Ca_1 + Ga_2 = ta_3 \qquad (3.10)$$

where:
C = weight of cereal fed
G = weight of grass consumed
t = total weight of faeces produced e.g derived from $Cr_2O_3$ procedures.
$a_1, a_2, a_3$ = concentration of markers in cereals, grass and total faeces, respectively.

By manipulation:

$$G = \frac{ta_3 - Ca_1}{a_2} \qquad (3.11)$$

These calculations will be discussed later in this chapter when used with the n-alkane technique.

## 3.5 WEIGHING TECHNIQUE

Weighing animals to estimate intake over short periods was suggested by Erizian (1932):

$$Intake = (Wt_2 + F + U + IWL) - Wt_1 - L \qquad (3.12)$$

where:
$Wt_1$ and $Wt_2$ are live weights before and after a period of grazing,
F and U are the weights of faeces and urine voided during the period
IWL is the 'insensible loss of weight'
L is the weight of water drunk.

This method was used in a slightly modified form by Allden and Young (1964) and with the development of accurate electronic balances has been developed further by Penning and Hooper (1985) for sheep and Huckle *et al.* (1994) for dairy cows. Basically, to use this technique animals are harnessed to prevent faeces and urine losses, weighed, allowed to graze for about one hour, and reweighed. Insensible weight loss (IWL) is determined by weighing the animals, preventing them from eating for about 1 hour and weighing them again after this period of fasting. The loss of weight in this period gives an estimate of IWL. Change in live weight after eating plus the IWL gives the weight of fresh herbage intake. The component parts of the technique are described below.

## 3.5.1 Weighing the animals

Modern electronic balances allow animals to be weighed accurately. Penning and Hooper (1985) used a balance which output weights via an RS232 serial port at 5 per second to a portable computer and a running mean and standard error were calculated by a computer program. This overcomes the problems in weight fluctuations due to movement by animals when they are being weighed. The precision of the weighing can be controlled by entering a minimum number of weighings, a predetermined standard error and/or a maximum number of weighings into the computer program used. This enabled sheep to be weighed with a precision of ± 10 g. Huckle *et al.* (1994) used a similar weighing method with dairy cows which enabled them to be weighed with a precision of ± 60 g. Romney *et al.* (1996) weighed goats using a battery powered balance with a built in animal weighing program with a precision of ± 60 g.

All the above balances were platform scales and crushes had to be fitted to the platforms to hold the animals. More recently weigh beams have been used which enable crushes to hold the animals to be fitted more easily. These have been used (S. M. Rutter personal communication) to weigh cows. Weigh beams can be battery powered and can also output weights to portable computers to help remove variations in weight due to movement.

When weighing animals with this precision it is necessary to construct wind breaks around the balance to minimise weight fluctuations due to air movements.

### 3.5.2 Insensible weigh loss (IWL)

The history of IWL dates back to first century when Eristatus carried out experiments into 'insensible perspiration' using chickens (quoted by Winslow and Herrington, 1949). Sanctorius in 1614 published accounts of his own 'insensible perspiration' measured by sitting on a steel yard for some hours and observing his own weight change (quoted by Winslow and Herrington, 1949). Insensible weight loss in grazing animals is mainly due to evaporative-respiratory cooling, sweating and the loss of gasses due to respiration and digestion. Kleiber (1961) stressed the importance of an accurate estimate of IWL to the weighing technique when it is used to estimate intake. Some examples of IWL are given in Table 3.3. However, it is not possible to estimate IWL whilst the animals are actually grazing and various techniques have been used to overcome this difficulty.

Allden (1962) and Allden and Whittaker (1970) measured IWL on one group of sheep whilst another group of sheep grazed and their weight change was recorded. The weight changes of individual animals in the grazing group were then adjusted using the mean IWL measured.

Penning and Hooper (1985) measured IWL on sheep for 1 hour before they were allowed to graze and then used each animal as its own control to adjust its weight change after grazing. Whilst Gibb et al. (1998) estimated IWL over 1 hour after grazing and again used individual animals as their own controls to correct live-weight changes during grazing for IWL. Table 3.3 shows how IWL is affected by ambient temperature. Dumont et al. (1994) not only found a correlation between air temperature and IWL but also with live weight, from these results and consistent between animal differences, Dumont et al. (1994) concluded that intake rate should be corrected for IWL measured on the same animals as used in the grazing phase of the technique. Penning and Hooper (1985) using sheep and Nuthall et al. (1994) using cattle found that IWL also increased with walking and Newman et al. (1994) found that

Table 3.3. Some measurements of insensible weight loss by ruminants measured at different air temperatures.

| | Dry ewes[1] | | Lactating cows[2] | | Dry goats[3] | |
|---|---|---|---|---|---|---|
| Air temperature (°C) | 13.6 | 15.8 | 14.3 | 30.8 | 22.9 | 28.4 |
| Insensible weight loss (g min⁻¹) | 2.1 | 5.0 | 16.0 | 29.1 | 1.2 | 2.3 |

[1]Penning and Hooper (1985), [2]Gibb et al. (1998) and [3]Romney et al. (1996).

fasting affected intake rate and diet selection. To take into account the above findings, the following method, currently in use at IGER, is suggested for estimating IWL:

i.    IWL is measured on the same animals as used to measure IR, **after** their period of grazing.
ii.   To estimate IWL animals are muzzled, weighed and returned to their plots for the same length of time as the grazing period.
iii.  They are then brought back to the weighing area and weighed again.
iv.   If there are major differences in temperature between the grazing period and period when IWL is measured, adjustments to rate of IWL may be made.

### 3.5.3 Calculating intake rate

Intake rate is calculated by fitting the animals with bags to collect all faeces and urine voided and animals may also be fitted with automatic behaviour recording equipment (Chapter 6). It is easier to use female animals as urine and dung can be collected in the same bag. Absorbents such as sodium bentonite or dried peat moss may be added to the bags to help prevent loss of urine. The animals are weighed ($W_1$) and the time of weighing ($t_1$) recorded, they are then returned to their plots for approximately 1h. Animals are weighed again ($W_2$) and the time of weighing recorded ($t_2$). Dung bags are emptied, if necessary, and muzzles to prevent grazing are fitted. Animals are weighed again ($W_3$) and the time noted ($t_3$), they are then returned to their plots and allowed to remain there for a time similar to that when they were allowed to graze. They are then brought back to the weighing area, weighed again ($W_4$) and the time of this weighing recorded ($t_4$). Equipment is then removed from the animals and they are returned to their treatment plots. Intake rate (g fresh herbage per minute eating) is then calculated as:

$$IR = \left( \frac{W_2 - W_1}{t_2 - t_1} + \frac{W_3 - W_4}{t_4 - t_3} \right) \bullet \left( \frac{t_2 - t_1}{ET} \right) \tag{3.13}$$

where all weights are measured in g and time in minutes and ET is eating time.

Pluck samples of herbage are taken, dried and then ashed, to convert intake rate to dry matter or organic matter. The automatic behaviour recording equipment can be used to estimate eating time (ET, min). If automatic behaviour recording equipment is not available grazing time will have to be recorded by manual observation. The difference between eating time (ET) and grazing time (GT) is discussed in Chapter 6 and below.

### 3.5.4 Interpretation of intake rate

In the above calculation intake rate was measured over 1 h, whilst sheep may graze for 12 h per day (Penning *et al.,* 1991) and dairy cows for 11 h per day ( Gibb *et al.,* 1998). This grazing time is made up of a series of grazing bouts (meals) (Rook and Huckle, 1997; Tollkamp *et al.,*1998 and Gibb *et al.,* 1998 ). These meals are of different lengths with the longest meal occurring in the evening (Orr *et al.,* 2001a and Rook *et al.,* 1994). Daily intake may be calculated by multiplying IR by GT or eating time

(Chapter 6), however, this is problematic and assumes that intake rate is constant (i) within a meal and (ii) between meals (over the day).

i.   Classically, cumulative intake within a meal has been found to be a negatively-accelerated function of time since the start of a meal (Le Mangen, 1971), similar shaped intake curves have been reported for housed ruminants (Forbes *et al.*, 1972; Aitchison, 1985 and Baumont *et al.*, 1989). Orr *et al.*, (2001b) also found that intake rate within a meal, by grazing sheep, decreased because of an increase in the number of short intra-meal intervals as the duration of the meal increased, resulting in a fall in intake rate. These intra-meal intervals can be measured and removed by the behaviour recording equipment described in Chapter 6, giving a measure of eating time. Intake rate within a meal, plotted against **eating time**, has been found to be constant within a meal (Orr *et al.*, 2001b) and therefore, using eating rate, rather than grazing time (eating time including intra-meal intervals) overcomes the problem of changing rates of intake within a meal.

ii.  Intake rate has been shown to vary over the day (Table 3.4) (Orr *et al.*, 1997; Gibb *et al.*, 1998 and Barrett *et al.*, 2001). These increases in intake rate are associated with increases in DM content of the herbage over the day. In addition Table 3.4 shows how intake rate falls as sward surface height is reduced under rotational grazing. Thus, calculating daily intake from a single measurement of IR can give rise to differences in estimates of daily herbage DM intake of up to 35% (Table 3.4). To overcome these changes in IR it is suggested that IR should be determined in the morning and evening and a weighting factor for change in intake rate calculated. Thus intake for each meal may then be calculated from IR and meal duration. Intakes for each meal can then be summed to give an estimate of daily intake rate.

## 3.5.5 Conclusion

The weighing technique can provide estimates of intake rate over relatively short periods which is particularly useful where sward conditions are changing rapidly as under rotational grazing. In addition, combined with the automatic behaviour recording equipment described in Chapter 6, the technique can be used to provide estimates of bite mass and obviates the need for surgically prepared animals. As there is no absolute measure of herbage intake by grazing animals it is difficult to assess the accuracy of this method to estimate daily herbage intake, However, comparisons between herbage intake under continuous stocking, made using this technique and the $Cr_2O_3$ technique, gave similar estimates of intake (Table 3.5).

## 3.6 N-ALKANES

The n-alkane technique to estimate herbage intake by grazing animals was developed by Mayes *et al.* (1986a) and has been described in detail in an excellent review by Dove and Mayes (1991). Long-chain N-alkanes are present in plant cuticular waxes and are predominantly of odd-chain length in the range $C_{25}$-$C_{35}$ with nonacosane ($C_{29}$), hentriacontane ($C_{31}$) and tritriacontane ($C_{33}$) being the most

*Table 3.4 Some effects of time of day on bite mass and herbage intake rate by grazing cows and sheep.*

| Animal | Sward Surface Height (SSH, cm) and treatment | Time of day (British Summer Time) | | | | Significance of trend | Reference |
|---|---|---|---|---|---|---|---|
| | | 0600-0730 | 1100-1130 | 1400-1600 | 1800-1930 | | |
| | | Intake rate (g DM min⁻¹ grazing) | | | | | |
| Sheep | SSH 6 (cm) Continuous stocking | 2.5 | 2.3 | 3.2 | 3.2 | Quadratic * | Orr *et al.* (1997) |
| Dairy Cows | SSH 18 (cm) Continuous stocking | 32.0 | 33.0 | 32.0 | 37.0 | NS | Barrett *et al.* (2001) |
| Dairy Cows | SSH 6.5 (cm) Continuous stocking | 17.1 | 18.0 | 24.0 | 23.0 | Linear ** | Gibb *et al.* (1998) |
| Dairy Cows | SSH (23.8-13.0 cm) Rotational stocking | 33.5 | 28.7 | 18.2 | 11.0 | Quadratic* | Barrett *et al.* (2001) |

abundant (Mayes *et al.*, 1986a). Although the recovery of alkanes in the faeces of grazing animals is incomplete, Mayes *et al.* (1986a) argued that incomplete recovery would not matter if animals were dosed with synthetic even-chain alkanes as external markers, for the estimation of faecal output, provided that adjacent pairs of odd-chain and even-chain alkanes had similar faecal recoveries. An example calculation to estimate intake using this technique is given in Equation 3.14

$$I_H = \frac{D_{32}}{\frac{F_{32}}{F_i} \cdot H_i - H_{32}} \qquad\qquad 3.14$$

where:
$I_H$ is daily herbage intake (kg/day);
$D_{32}$ is the weight of dosed even-chain alkane $C_{32}$ (mg/d);
$F_i$ is the concentration of alkane of chain length i in faeces (mg/kg DM);
$H$ is the concentration of alkane of chain length i in herbage (mg/kg DM);
$H_{32}$ is the concentration of alkane of chain length $C_{32}$ in the herbage (mg/kg DM).

Not only can the technique be used to estimate intake by grazing animals but it can also be used to estimate dietary composition and its digestibility. Equation 3.14 can be modified to estimate herbage intake of grazing animals receiving supplements, if their alkane composition, is known or they do not contain significant amounts of alkanes Hameleers and Mayes (1998). The component parts of the technique are described below.

Table 3.5. *Daily herbage Organic Matter Intakes (kg) by sheep grazing continuously stocked ryegrass swards using two different techniques. (Penning and Hooper, 1985).*

| | Sward Surface Height (cm) | | | |
| --- | --- | --- | --- | --- |
| | 3 | 6 | 9 | 12 |
| Herbage intake using $Cr_2O_3$ technique | 1.60 | 2.98 | 2.75 | 2.54 |
| Herbage intake using weighing technique | 1.85 | 3.06 | 2.75 | 2.49 |

3.6.1 Recovery rates of dosed and naturally occurring alkanes

Equation 3.14 shows that the accuracy of the technique depends on the dosed and naturally occurring alkanes having similar recovery rates. Alkane $C_{32}$ (dosed) and $C_{33}$ (natural) have similar recovery rates (Table 3.6) but all alkanes had incomplete recoveries. Mayes *et al.* (1988) showed that the incomplete recovery of alkanes was due, mainly, to absorption of alkanes in the small intestine and that negligible synthesis of alkanes took place in the gut. Where possible the $C_{32}$ and $C_{33}$ pair of alkanes are preferred for estimating intake but if $C_{33}$ concentrations in the herbage are low then using $C_{31}$:$C_{32}$ may be preferable.

*Table 3.6. Recovery rates of naturally occurring and dosed synthetic alkanes.*

n-alkane

| $C_{27}$ | $C_{28}$[*] | $C_{29}$ | $C_{30}$[*] | $C_{31}$ | $C_{32}$[*] | $C_{33}$ | $C_{35}$ | $C_{36}$[*] | Reference |
|---|---|---|---|---|---|---|---|---|---|
| 0.713 | 0.768 | 0.745 | 0.820 | 0.854 | 0.889 | 0.891 | 0.931 | - | Mayes et al. (1986a) |
| 0.594 | 0.786 | 0.697 | - | 0.779 | 0.859 | 0.839 | 0.953 | 0.922 | Mayes et al. (1988) |
| - | - | - | - | 0.833 | 0.865 | 0.853 | 0.884 | 0.905 | Dillon and Stakelum (1988) |
| | 0.930 | 0.910 | 0.960 | 0.930 | 0.880 | 0.880 | 0.910 | 0.860 | Vullich et al. (1991) |
| 0.753 | - | 0.767 | - | 0.826 | 0.861 | 0.838 | 0.882 | - | Dillon (1993) |
| 0.801 | - | 0.871 | 0.871 | 0.900 | 0.927 | 0.917 | 0.937 | 0.933 | Molle et al. (1998) |
| - | - | - | - | 0.869 | 0.896 | 0.851 | - | - | Piasentier et al. (1995) |

[*] Dosed alkanes

3.6.1.1 *Methods for preparation of dosed alkanes.* The preparation of doses of alkanes is laborious and several methods have been developed to try reduce the labour requirements in their preparation, these are listed below:

i.   Paper boluses. Alkanes are dissolved in a heated solution of n-heptane and this solution is added to a tray containing warmed filter papers. The filter papers are then allowed to dry in a fume cupboard and after drying placed in an oven at 100°C for 2 min. When cool the paper is shredded with a guillotine and individual doses weighed and wrapped in tissue paper. (Mayes *et al.,* 1986a).

ii.  Gelatine capsules. Caps are removed from capsules (14mm ID x 21-25 mm, Kruger, Germany) and capsules are placed in racks. Each capsule is half filled with powdered cellulose. A solution of alkanes in heptane such that 1 ml will contain sufficient alkane to provide half of each days dose (if two capsules per day are to be dosed) is prepared and heated to dissolve the alkanes and then maintained at 55°C. 1 ml of alkane solution is pipetted onto the cellulose powder in each capsule. Capsules are left for 24 h, to allow solvent to evaporate, and then their caps are replaced and held in place with small pieces of sticky tape. (Dove *et al.,* 1988). A variation of this technique is described by Vullich *et al.* (1991) where a weight equivalent of cellulose fibre and alkane is dissolved in n-heptane. This is homogenised and evaporated in a rotary evaporator and the dried powder is filled into gelatine capsules.

iii. Paper bungs. Pure cellulose laboratory stoppers (Celloplug, PBI, diameter 8-14mm, length, 15 mm) are loosened by gently rolling between finger and thumb, placed in metal racks and heated at 100°C for 30 min. Racks are removed from the oven and place on a hotplate. Then using a similar method to that for preparing gelatine capsules, the alkane solution is pipetted onto the end of each bung. The solvent is allowed to evaporate and the bungs are placed in oven at 100°C for 20 min to melt the alkane into the bung. The whole process may be repeated to increase the alkane concentration in each bung. (R.W. Mayes, personal communication; Molle *et al.*, 1998).

iv.   Liquid suspension. Grass is dried and milled to pass through a 1 mm sieve and the soluble fraction is extracted with water. The grass is then dried again and coated with alkanes on a rotary evaporator. 75 g of treated grass is suspended in 3 kg water containing 0.4% xanthum gum (Keltrol GM, Merck & Co). Sheep were dosed with 40 ml volumes of alkane suspension using a disposable syringe and a dosing gun, delivering 50-100 ml, was used for cattle (Marais *et al.*, 1996).

v.    Controlled Release Devices (CRDs). These devices are manufactured commercially by Captec NZ, P O Box 75340 Manurewa, Auckland NZ (similar to those described for $Cr_2O_3$, 3.3.2.1) and deliver a controlled dose of alkanes ($C_{32}$) for approximately 21 days. Tests with sheep (Mayes *et al.*, 1991, Mayes *et al.*, 1995) have shown that they can be used to give accurate estimates of intake. Dove *et al.* (2002) found that, in rumen-fistulated sheep, release rate of alkanes from CRDs was linear and reached a constant rate after 2-3 days. Release rate of alkanes was close to the manufacturers stated rate for the CRDs of 40 mg/day and alkanes reached plateau concentrations in the faeces 6-7 days after dosing. There was no effect of level of feeding on release rate of alkanes. Faecal concentrations of alkanes arising from CRDs were less variable than $C_{36}$ administered in paper pelettes as a single daily dose. Molle *et al.* (1998) also evaluated the use of CRDs and concluded they gave reliable estimates of intake and greatly reduced labour requirements by obviating the need to prepare alkane doses and by reducing animal handling. However, it is recommended that if CRDs containing alkanes are used, then checks listed in 3.3.2.4 above should be applied.

Some comparison of herbage intake using the different methods for preparing alkane doses are given in Table 3.7. Molle *et al.* (1998) concluded that different dosing procedures were equally satisfactory except that gelatine capsules, dosed once daily gave a slightly lower accuracy than twice daily dosing. Molle *et al.* (1998), Mayes *et al.* (1988) found high faecal recovery rates for $C_{36}$ and Mayes *et al.* (1995) suggested that if animals were dosed with both $C_{32}$ and $C_{36}$, intake and faecal output and diet digestibility could be determined using a single analytical procedure.

3.6.1.2 *Dosing and faeces sampling regimes.* Unlike the $Cr_2O_3$ technique the absolute recovery of alkanes is not necessary but the important factor is whether there is diurnal variation in the ratio of the dosed to the naturally occurring alkane (Equation 3.14). The validity of this assumption has been extensively reviewed by Dove and Mayes (1991). Mayes *et al.* (1986a) dosed housed sheep twice daily with paper pellets and did not find any variation in faecal alkane ratios, whilst Dove *et al.* (2002) found variation with time in the alkane ratio of $C_{35}:C_{36}$ when $C_{36}$ was dosed once daily in paper pellets. Dove *et al.* (1989) dosed grazing sheep twice daily with gelatine capsules containing alkanes, they compared alkane concentrations in rectal samples of faeces, taken twice daily, with concentrations in total faeces. They concluded temporal variation in alkane concentrations was not a problem. Sibbald *et al.* (2000) found little diurnal variation in concentrations of natural alkanes in faeces samples taken at three hour intervals.

3.7. *Some results from indoor feeding experiments showing mean differences between actual herbage DM intake and estimated DM intake using dosed $C_{32}$ (dosed) and $C_{33}$ (naturally occurring) alkanes.*

| Animals and diets | Method of dosing | Mean actual DM Intake g/d | Mean difference[1] g/d | Reference |
|---|---|---|---|---|
| **Sheep** | | | | |
| Fresh perennial ryegrass | Shredded paper[2] | 579 | 0 | Mayes et al. (1986a) |
| Frozen-stored perennial ryegrass | CRD[3] | 914 | 0 | Mayes et al. (1991) |
| Fresh herbage | Gelatine capsule[4] | 778 | 20 | Vullich (1991) |
| Fresh Italian ryegrass | CRD | 666 | 24 | Molle et al. (1998) |
| ditto | Paper bung[5] | 634 | 19 | ditto |
| ditto | Gelatine capsule[6] | 685 | 31 | ditto |
| ditto | Gelatine capsule[7] | 662 | -22 | ditto |
| **Cattle** | | | | |
| Fresh grass | Shredded paper | 4000 | -70 | Mayes et al. (1986b) |
| Fresh perennial ryegrass | Shredded paper | 13700 | 50 | Data of Dillon and Stakelum[8] |
| ditto | ditto | 12390 | 350 | ditto |
| ditto | Gelatine capsule | 12640 | -960 | ditto |

[1] Mean actual intake - Mean predicted intake;
[2] Pellet of shredded paper impregnated with $C_{32}$ alkane;
[3] Controlled release device containing $C_{32}$ alkane;
[4] Gelatine capsule containing cellulose powder coated with $C_{32}$ alkane;
[5] Cellulose laboratory stopper coated with $C_{32}$ alkane;
[6] Gelatine capsule dosed once per day;
[7] Gelatine capsule dosed twice per day;
[8] Quoted by Mayes et al. (1995).

These workers found that dosing alkanes in paper pellets once a day, to housed sheep fed grass pellets, gave slightly less variable results than with twice a day dosing of alkanes. Molle *et al.* (1998) found a slightly lower accuracy of intake estimation using once-daily dosed compared with twice-daily dosed gelatine capsules containing alkanes and Mayes *et al.* (1995), reported gross over-estimates of intake by deer dosed once daily with gelatine capsules containing alkanes and cellulose powder. Piasentier *et al.* (1995) found that dosing sheep once per day with alkanes in paper pellets underestimated intake by 3%.

For dairy cows, greater variation in faecal concentration of alkanes was found after once-daily compared with twice-daily dosing (Dillon and Stakelum 1989, 1990; Stakelum and Dillon 1990) but later studies Dillon and Stakelum (1990) and Stakelum and Dillon (1990) found less marked variation in faecal alkane concentrations.

Vullich and Hanrahan (1995) reported that once-daily grab sampling of faeces gave an overestimate of intake, whilst for twice-daily grab sampling, there was no significant difference in the precision of intake estimation compared with total faeces collection.

Duncan *et al.* (1999) used n-alkanes to estimate short-term diet composition in sheep and concluded that precise estimates could be obtained following consumption of simple herbage mixtures over 24-48 h. In addition they found that intake could be estimated using this technique provided that a series of faecal samples were collected over 4-5 days following the period of ingestion.

From the above results no clear recommendations can be drawn but it is tentatively suggested that animals are dosed twice per day and faeces samples collected at the same time as dosing. Any of the methods described above for preparing doses of alkanes appear satisfactory. As with the $Cr_2O_3$ technique, a period of about 12 days is required to estimate intake, comprising a preliminary dosing period of 6-7 days for the dosed alkane to equilibrate throughout the gut, followed by faeces sampling over the last 5 days. Using CRDs together with sampling of faeces from the pasture (3.3.2.2 ) will greatly reduce disturbance to the grazing animals and labour requirements, compared with other procedures.

3.6.1.3 *Pasture Sampling.* Accurate estimates of alkane concentrations of the herbage consumed by the grazing animals are essential to this technique (Equation 3.14). Methods of herbage sampling have already been described in section 3.4.4 and these apply equally to sampling to estimating alkane concentrations in the diet of grazing animals. Vulich *et al.* (1993) compared alkane concentrations in clipped, hand-plucked and extrusa samples of herbage collected from a permanent pasture and concluded that there was little difference between methods. Dove *et al.* (1996) showed that alkane concentrations varied with both plant species and botanical components within plants and, because of this, Dove and Mayes (1991) suggested more herbage samples may be required to give accurate estimates of alkane concentrations in the diet than are required to estimate *in vitro* digestibility, particularly when using fistulated animals.

3.6.1.4 *Processing samples and chemical analysis.* Samples of herbage and faeces should be freeze dried if possible. Dove and Mayes (1991) showed that oven drying at

100°C reduced the concentrations of alkanes in the samples, although this effect was still present in samples dried at 70°C, it was less marked. If freeze-drying facilities are not available then drying at 60°C to constant dry weight is suggested (H. Dove personal communication). After drying samples should be ground to pass through a 1 mm sieve. Various sample sizes have been used in the analysis and it suggested that 0.5 to 3.0 g of herbage and 0.5 to 1.5 g of faeces is adequate. If alkane concentrations are low then the larger samples are used to increase concentrations of the alkanes in the samples extracted for analysis.

The original gas chromatography method for alkane analysis was described by Mayes *et al.* (1986a). Alkanes were removed by solvent extraction followed by saponification of the abstract in 1M alcoholic KOH to remove fatty acids. As the $C_{34}$ alkane is not present in herbage or faeces this was used as an internal standard whilst Oliván *et al.* (1994) suggested the use of two internal standards. Dove and Mayes (1991) found that the extraction step could be omitted and the samples saponified directly. Vulich *et al.* (1995) suggested further modifications to the technique which reduced the workload and costs of the analytical process. It is not possible to list here all the methods and modifications applied to the analysis and readers are referred to Mayes *et al.* (1986), Dove (1992), Vulich *et al.* (1995) and Duncan *et al.* (1999) for detailed descriptions of the technique.

3.6.1.5 *Estimating diet composition and digestibility.* Methods for estimating the botanical composition of the diet of grazing animals have been reviewed by Holechek (1982) and Norbury and Sansom (1992) These methods generally involve the identification of plant fragments in samples of faeces or extrusa and are extremely laborious, require trained observers and relationships between plant area and mass are required to obtain gravimetric estimates of diet composition. Although the ratio of $^{13}C:^{12}C$ has been used to determine the dietary proportions of mixtures of $C_3$ and $C_4$ plants in the diet of grazing animals (Jones *et al.,* 1979*)* until the use of alkanes no satisfactory chemical marker to estimate diet composition for mixtures of $C_3$ plants or mixtures of $C_4$ plants had been identified.

There are differences between plant species in the pattern of alkanes in cuticular waxes Mayes and Dove (1991), Dove (1992), Mayes *et al.* (1995) and Dove *et al.* (1996). Dove and Mayes (1991) suggested that diet composition could be estimated by measuring these alkane patterns in the herbage and faeces and could also be used to determine the species composition of herbage mixtures or composition of extrusa samples.

Diet composition of grazing animals may be calculated from the concentrations of alkanes in the dietary components and faeces, taking into account the recovery rates of the alkanes. Values for recovery rates may be taken from the literature (Table 3.6) or preferably some animals on the experiment should be dosed with the range of alkanes used; total faeces collected and recovery rates calculated. Theoretically it is possible to determine the same number of components in the diet as the number of alkanes used.

Various mathematical methods have been used to calculate dietary composition, Dove and Mayes (1991) suggested the use of simultaneous equations, Newman *et al.*

(1995) used a least squares estimation of diet composition, Salt *et al.* (1994) used an iterative algorithm (Microsoft© Excel, Solver) and Dove and More (1996) used a non-negative least squares algorithm. The disadvantage of using simultaneous equations is that to estimate a two component diet the problem exists of which pair of alkanes to choose and choosing different pairs of alkanes may yield different answers (Newman *et al.,* 1995). The method described by Newman *et al.* (1995) is only suitable for a two component diet, whilst the method used by Salt *et al.* (1994) uses relatively complex non-linear approximation. The method of Dove and More (1996) can be used to determine the composition of diets containing several species of herbage and allows the application of non-negativity constraints to be applied to the solutions. A computer program to perform these calculations 'Eatwhat' is described by Dove and More (1996) and copies may be obtained from these workers.

Hameleers and Mayes (1998) compared the methods of Salt *et al.* (1994), Newman *et al.* (1995) and Dove and More (1996) to calculate the amounts of clover and grass ingested by cows, they found little difference between estimates using the three methods of calculation, and actual diet composition. Total intakes were then estimated using mean alkane concentrations in the ingested herbage calculated from the estimated proportions of white clover and grass in the diet.

Dove and Mayes (1991) pointed out that if concentrations of alkanes in herbage and faeces (mg/kg) are used as units of measurement, then the solutions to dietary composition will yield the weight of herbage species consumed required to produce 1 kg of faeces. Thus, from this, it is possible to calculate digestibility of each herbage component and the overall digestibility of the diet. On a cautionary note, Newman *et al.* (1998) carried out a sensitivity analysis on the use of the n-alkane technique in the study of diet composition and concluded, amongst other things, that in the face of any sort of measurement error, estimates of digestibility are likely to be unreliable. These workers suggested that the application of a bias correction technique, such as the bootstrap, would be a worthwhile modification to the present statistical techniques.

The main problem with validating this technique in the field is that no absolute measure of diet selection exists. However, (R.A.Champion, personal communication) compared estimates of grass and clover intake by sheep grazing coterminal areas of grass or clover by observing the proportion of time the sheep spent grazing grass or clover and their diet composition using the alkane technique (Table 3.8). This shows that both methods gave estimates of dietary composition that differed by approximately 5%.

## 3.7 CONCLUSIONS AND FUTURE DEVELOPMENTS

Since the first edition of this book there have been major advances in the development of techniques to estimate intake by grazing animals. The alkane technique in the UK, at least, has displaced chromic oxide as the method most commonly used to estimate intake. In addition, considerable development and improvements to the weighing technique have taken place.

The weighing technique is best suited to estimating intake over short periods (hours) and can be used where sward state is changing rapidly, whilst the alkane

*Table 3.8. Comparisons of diet composition of sheep grazing coterminous areas of grass and clover using alkanes or by observation of grazing time.*

| Method of diet estimation. | Plots 50% Grass: 50% Clover by area | |
|---|---|---|
| | Plot 1 | Plot 2 |
| N-alkanes. Proportion of clover DM in the diet calculated using the 'Eatwhat' program. | 0.68 | 0.55 |
| Proportion of total grazing time grazing clover. | 0.69 | 0.44 |
| Proportion of total daily DM intake as clover* | 0.73 | 0.49 |

* Total DM intake estimated from grazing time x intake rate of each herbage species.

technique is more suited to estimating intake and diet selection over longer periods (days), where sward state is relatively stable.

Further improvement to the weighing technique could be achieved by using it, together with behaviour recording equipment (Chapter 6), to estimate meals and eating rates within these meals over the day, and thus improve its accuracy in estimating daily intake.

The use of other internal markers in herbage such as fatty alcohols and alkenes (Mayes *et al.,* 1998) are being investigated and these may provide additional markers that could be used alone, or as additional to alkanes, to provide improvements in estimating intake and diet selection.

## 3.8 REFERENCES

AITCHISON E.M. (1985) A study of the removal of fibre from the rumen and voluntary intake of sheep eating hay diets. *PhD Thesis, University of Reading.*

ALEXANDER R.H. and McGOWAN M. (1966) The routine determination of the *in vitro* digestibility of organic matter in forages. An investigation of the problems associated with continuous large-scale operation. *Journal of the British Grassland Society,* **21**, 140-147.

ALLDEN W.G. (1962) Rate of herbage intake and grazing time in relation to herbage availability. *Proceedings of the Australian Society of Animal Production,* **4**, 163-166.

ALLDEN W.G. and WHITTAKER I.A. McD. (1970) The determinants of herbage intake by grazing sheep. The interrelationship of factors influencing herbage intake and availability. *Australian Journal of Agricultural Research,* **21**, 755-766.

ALLDEN W.G. and YOUNG R.S. (1964) The summer nutrition of weaner sheep: Herbage intake following periods of different nutrition. *Australian Journal of Agricultural Research,* **15**, 989-1000.

BALDOCK N.M. (1985) Heart rate and behaviour recorded in sheep during undisturbed conditions and various husbandry practices. *Ph D. Thesis University of Reading.* pp 141.

BARNES R.F. (1967) Collaborative *in vitro* rumen fermentation studies on forage substrates. *Journal of Animal Science,* **26**, 1120-1130.

BARRETT P.D., LAIDLAW A.S., MAYNE C.S. and CHRISTIE H. (2001) Patterns of herbage intake rate and bite dimensions of rotationally grazed dairy cows as sward height declines. *Grass and Forage Science,* **56**, 362-373.

BARTHIAUX-THILL N. and OGER R. (1986) The indirect estimation of the digestibility in cattle of herbage from Belgian permanent pasture. *Grass and Forage Science,* **41**, 269-272.

BAUMONT R., BRUN J. P., and DULPHY J.P. (1989) Influence of the nature of hay on its ingestibility and the kinetics of intake during large meals in sheep and cows. *Proceedings of the 16th International Grassland Congress,* Nice, France, pp. 15-28.

BLAXTER K.L. (1961) The utilisation of energy of food by ruminants. *Proceedings of the 2nd Symposium on Energy Metabolism. EAAP Publication No 100,* pp. 211-225.

BLAXTER K.L., WAINMAN F.W. and DAVIDSON J.L. (1966) The voluntary intake of food by sheep and cattle in relation to their energy requirements for maintenance. *Animal Production,* **8**, 75-83.

BOVAL M., PEYRAUD J.L., XANDÉ A., AUMONT G., COPPRY O., and SAINADIN G. (1996) Evaluation d'indicateurs fécaux pour la prediction de la digestibilité et des quantités ingérées de Dichantium sp. par des bovines créoles en Guadeloupe. *Annales de Zootechnie,* **45**, 121-134.

BROWN E. and DUVAL J.W.T. (1907) A quick method for the determination of moisture in grain. *USDA Bureau of Plant Industry,* Bulletin No. 99.

BRUCKENTAL I., LEHRER A.R., WEITZ M., BERNARD J. KENNIT H. and NEUMARK H. (1987) Faecal output and estimated voluntary dry-matter intake of grazing beef cows, relative to their live weight and to the digestibility of the pasture. *Annimal Production,* **45**, 23-28.

BURNS J.C., POND R.K. and FISHER D.S. (1994) Measurement of forage intake. In: Fahey J.C. (ed.). *Forage quality, evaluation and utilization.* Wisconsin, U.S.A. American Society of Agronomy, Inc., pp. 494-532.

CAMMELL S.B. (1977) Equipment and techniques used for research into intake and digestion of forages by sheep and calves. *Grassland Research Institute Technical Report, No. 24.*

CHAMERLAIN D.G. and THOMAS P.C. (1983) A note on the use of chromium sesquioxide as a marker in nutritional experiments with dairy cows. *Animal Production,* **36**, 155-157.

CHENOST M. (1985) Estimation de la digestibilité de l'herbe ingéré au pârturage à partir de l'azote fécal et de quelques autres parameters fécaux. *Annales de Zootechnie,* **34**, 205-228.

CLEMENTS R.J., JONES R.M., VALDES L.R. and BUNCH G.A. (1996) Selection of *Chamaecrista rotundifolia* by cattle. *Tropical Grasslands,* **30**, 389-394.

COATES D.B. and PENNING P.D. (2000) Measuring animal performance. In: 't Mannetje L. and Jones R.M. (eds). *Field and laboratory methods for grassland and animal production research.* Wallingford U.K.: CABI, pp. 353-402.

COATES D.B., SCHACHENMANN P. and JONES R.J. (1987) Reliability of extrusa samples collected from steers fistulated at the oesophagus to estimate the diet of resident animals in grazing experiments. *Australian Journal of Experimental Agriculture,* **27**, 739-745.

COMMONWEALTH AGRICULTURAL BUREAUX. (1961) Research techniques in use at the Grassland Research Institute, Hurley. *Bulletin 45, Publication Commonwealth Bureaux of Pasture Field Crops,* Farnham Royal, Bucks, UK.

COSTIGAN P. and ELLIS K.J. (1987) Analysis of faecal chromium derived from controlled release marker devices. *New Zealand Journal of Technology,* **3**, 89-92.

COMERON E.A. and PEYRAUD J.L. (1993) Prediction of herbage digestibility ingested by dairy cows. *Revue Argentine de Production Animale,* **13**, (1) 23-30.

CORBETT J.L., GREENHALGH J.F.D. and McDONALD A.P. (1958) Paper as a carrier for chromium sesquioxide. *Nature, London,* **182**, 1014-1016.

CORBETT J.L., GREENHALGH J.F.D. and FLORENCE E. (1959) Distribution of chromium sesquioxide and polyethyleneglycol in the reticulo-rumen of cattle. *British Journal of Nutrition,* **13**, 337-345.

CRUIKSHANK G.J., POPPI D.P. and SYKES A.R. (1987) Some factors affecting the accuracy of estimation of nutrient supply in grazing animals. *Proceedings of the 4th AAAP Animal Science Congress (Hamilton),* p. 332.

DELAGARDE R., PEYRAUD J.L. and DELABY L. (1999) Influence of carbohydrate or protein supplementation on intake, behaviour and digestion in dairy cows strip-grazing a low nitrogen fertilized sward. *Annales de Zootechnie,* **48**, 81-96.

DEMARQUILLY C. and JARRIGE R. (1981) Panorama des methods de prevision de la digestibilité et de la valeur énergétique des fourrages. In: INRA Publications (ed.). *Prévision de la valeur nutritive des aliments des ruminants.* Vesailles, France, 41-59.

DILLON P. (1993) The use of n-alkanes as markers to determine intake, botanical composition of available or consumed herbage in studies of digesta kinetics with dairy cows. *PhD Thesis, National University of Ireland, Dublin.*

DILLON P. and STAKELUM G. (1988) The use of n-alkanes and chromic oxide as markers for determining feed intake, faecal output and digestibility in dairy cows. *Proceedings of the 12th General Meeting of the European Grassland Federation,* Dublin, Ireland, pp. 154-158.

DILLON P. and STAKELUM G. (1989) Herbage and dosed alkanes as a grass measurement technique for dairy cows. *Irish Journal of Agricultural Research,* **28**, 104.

DILLON P. and STAKELUM G. (1990) Dosed and herbage alkanes for predicting silage intake with dairy cows. *Proceedings VII European Grazing Workshop,* Wageningen, The Netherlands, October 1990.

DONFER E., NIEMANN P.J., CRAMPTON E.W. and LLOYD L.E. (1963) Dry matter disappearance by enzyme and aqueous solutions to predict the nutritive value of forages. *Journal of Dairy Science,* **46**, 965-970.

DOVE H. (1992) Using the n-alkanes of plant cuticular wax to estimate the species composition of herbage mixtures. *Australian Journal of Agricultural Research,* **43**, 1711-1724.

DOVE H. and COOMBE J.B. (1992) A comparison of methods for estimating supplement intake and diet digestibility in sheep. *Proceedings Australian Society of Animal Production,* **19**, 239-241.

DOVE H., FREER M, and FOOT J.Z. (1988) Alkane capsules for measuring pasture intake. *Proceedings of the Nutritional Society of Australia,* **13**, 131.

DOVE H. and MAYES R.W. (1991) The use of plant alkanes as marker substances in studies of the nutrition of herbivores: a review. *Australian Journal of Agricultural Research,* **42**, 913-952.

DOVE H., MAYES R.W. and FREER M. (1996) Effects of species, plant-part, and plant-age on n-alkane concentrations in the cuticular wax of pasture plants. *Australian Journal of Agricultural Research,* **47**,1333-1347.

DOVE H., MAYES R.W., FREER M. and COOMBE J.B. (1989) Faecal recoveries of the alkanes of plant cuticular waxes in penned and grazing sheep. *Proceedings XVI International Grassland Congress,* Nice, France, pp. 1093-1094.

DOVE H., MAYES R.W., LAMB C.S. and ELLIS K.J. (2002) Factors influencing the release rate of alkanes from an intra-ruminal, controlled-release device, and the resultant accuracy of intake estimation in sheep. *Australian Journal of Agricultural Research,* **53**, 681-696.

DOVE H. and MOORE A.D. (1996) Using a least-squares optimisation procedure to estimate botanical composition based on alkanes of plant cuticular wax. *Australian Journal of Agricultural Research*, **46**, 1535-1544.

DOYLE P.T., CASSON T., CRANSBERG L., and ROWE J.B. (1994) Faecal output of grazing sheep measured by total collection or using chromium sesquioxide. *Small Ruminant Research*, **13**, 1333-1347.

DUMONT B. AND IAASON G.R. (2000) Can we believe the results of grazing experiments? Issues and limitations in methodology. In: ROOK A.J. AND PENNING P.D. (eds.) *The principles and practice of grazing, for profit and environmental gain, within temperate grassland systems. Proceedings of the British Grassland Society Occasional Symposium*, **34**, 171-180.

DUMONT B., PENNING P.D., ORR R.J. and D'HOUR P. (1994) Effects of some factors on insensible weight loss in grazing sheep. *Annales de Zootechnie*, **43**, 283.

DUNCAN A.J., MAYES R.W., LAMB C.S., YOUNG S.A. and CASTILLO I. (1999) The use of naturally occurring and artificially applied n-alkanes as markers for estimation of short-term diet composition and intake in sheep. *Journal Agricultural Science, Cambridge*, **132**, 233-246.

EDIN H. (1918), cited by Kotb and Luckey (1972) *Nutritional Abstracts and Reviews*, **42**, 813-845.

EL SHAER H.M., OMED H.M., CHAMERLAIN A.G. and AXFORD R.F.E. (1987) The use of faecal organisms from sheep for the *in vitro* determination of digestibility. *Journal of Agricultural Science, Cambridge*, **109**, 257-259.

ERIZIAN E. (1932) Eine neue Methode zur Bestimmung der vom Vieh gefressenen Menge Weidefutters. *Zeitschrift für Tierzüchtung und Züchtungsbiologie, Reihe B*, **25**, 443-459.

FISCHER K. (1935) Neues Verfahren zur massanalytischen Bestimmung des Wassergehaltes und festen Körpern. *Agnew Chem*, **487**, 394-396.

FORBES J.M., WRIGHT J.A. and BANNISTER A. (1972) A note on rate of eating in sheep. *Animal Production*, **15**, 211-214.

FRANCE J., DHANOA M.S., SIDDONS R.C., THORNLEY J.H.M. and POPPI D.P. (1988) Estimating the production of faeces by ruminants from faecal marker concentration curves. *Journal of Theoretical Biology*, **135**, 383-391.

FURNIVAL E.P., CORBETT J.L. and INSKIP M.W. (1990) Evaluation of controlled release devices for administration of chromium sesquioxide using fistulated grazing sheep. 1. Variation in marker concentration in faeces. *Australian Journal of Agricultural Research*, **41**, 969-975.

GIBB M.J., HUCKLE C.A. and NUTHALL R. (1998) Effect of time of day on grazing behaviour and intake rate by lactating dairy cows. *Grass and Forage Science*, **53**, 41-46.

GIVENS, D. I. AND DEAVILLE, E.R. (1999) The current role of near infrared spectroscopy in animal nutrition: a review. *Australian Journal of Agricultural Research*, **50**, 1131-1145.

GONZALES V. and LAMBOURNE J.L. (1966) Caracteristicas de la secrecion salivar de corderos alimentados con differentes forrajes y effectos de la saliva sobre la digestibilidad *in vitro* de los mismos. *Revista de Nutricion Animal*, **IV**, 34-40.

GREENHALGH J.F.D. (1982) An introduction to herbage intake measurements. In: Leaver J.D. (ed). *Herbage Intake Handbook*. Hurley U.K: British Grassland Society, pp. 1-10.

GREENHALGH J.F.D and CORBETT J.L. (1960) The indirect estimation of the digestibility of pasture herbage. 1. Nitrogen and chromogen as faecal index substances. *Journal of Agricultural Science, Cambridge*, **55**, 371-376.

GREENHALGH J.F.D., REID G.W., AITKEN J.N. and FLORENCE E. (1966a) The effects of grazing intensity on herbage consumption and animal production. 1. Short term effects in strip-grazed dairy cows. *Journal of Agricultural Science, Cambridge,* **67**, 13-23.

GREENHALGH J.F.D., REID G.W. and McDONALD I. (1966b) The indirect estimation of the digestibility of pasture herbage. 4 Regressions of digestibility on faecal nitrogen concentration: effects of different fractions of the herbage upon within-and between-period regressions. *Journal of Agricultural Science, Cambridge,* **66**, 277-283.

HAMELEERS A. and MAYES R.W. (1998) The use of n-alkanes to estimate herbage intake and diet composition by dairy cows offered a perennial ryegrass/white clover mixture. *Grass and Forage Science,* **53**, 164-169.

HAMILTON F.J., McMANUS W.R. and LARSEN L.H. (1960) An improved method of oesophageal fistulation for food intake studies in sheep. *Australian Veterinary Journal,* **36**, 111-112.

HARDISON W.A. and REID J.T. (1953) Use of indicators in the measurement of dry-matter intake of grazing animals. *Journal of Nutrition,* **51**, 35-52.

HATFIELD P.G., CLANTON D.C., SANSON D.W. and ESKRIDGE K.M. (1990) Methods of administering ytterbium for estimation of faecal output. *Journal of Range Management,* **43**, 316-320.

HATFIELD P.G., WALKER J.W. and GLIMP H.A. (1991) Comparing the captec bolus to chromic oxide dosed twice daily using sheep in confinement. *Journal of Range Management,* **44**, 408-409.

HEALY W.B. (1968) Ingestion of soil by dairy cows. *New Zealand Journal of Agricultural Research,* **11**, 487-499.

HODGSON J. and MAXWELL T.J. (1982) Grazing research and grazing management. *The Hill Farming Research Organisation Biennial Report 1979-1981,* pp. 169-187.

HOLECHEK J.L., VAVRA M. and PIEPER R.D. (1982) Botanical composition determination of range diets: a review. *Journal of Range Management,* **35**, 309-315.

HOLECHEK J.L., WOFFORD H., ARTHUN D., GALYAN M.L. and WALLACE J.D. (1986) Evaluation of total faecal collection for measuring cattle forage intake. *Journal of Range Management,* **39**, 2-4.

HUCKLE C.A., NUTHALL R. and GIBB M.J. (1994) The use of short-term weight changes to measure intake rates in grazing dairy cattle. *Fourth BGS Research Conference,* British Grassland Society, September 1994, pp. 157-158.

JONES D.I.H. and HAYWARD M.V. (1973) A cellulase digestion technique for predicting dry matter digestibility of grasses. *Journal of Science Food and Agriculture,* **24**, 1419-1426.

JONES D.I.H. and HAYWARD M.V. (1975) The effect of pepsin pre-treatment of herbage on the prediction of dry matter digestibility from solubility in fungal cellulase solutions. *Journal of Science Food and Agriculture,* **26**, 711-718.

JONES D.I.H. and MOSELEY G. (1993) Laboratory methods for estimating nutritive quality. In:. Davies A., Baker R.D., Grant S.A. and Laidlaw A.S.(eds). *Herbage Measurement Handbook (2nd edition)* British Grassland Society, Reading U.K. pp. 263-283.

JONES R.J. and LASCANO C.E. (1992) Oesophageal fistulated cattle can give unreliable estimates of the proportion of legume in the diets of resident animals grazing tropical pastures. *Grass and Forage Science,* **47**, 128-132.

JONES R.J., LUDLOW M.M., TROUGHTON J.H. and BLUNT C.G. (1979) Estimation of the proportion of $C_3$ and $C_4$ plant species in the diet of animals from the ratio of natural $^{12}C$ and $^{13}C$ isotopes in the faeces. *Journal of Agricultural Science, Cambridge,* **92**, 91-100.

KLEIBER M. (1961) *The fire of life: an introduction to animal energetics.* Published Wiley, New York. pp. 454.

KOTB A.R. and LUCKEY T.D. (1972) Markers in Nutrition. *Nutrition Abstracts and Reviews,* **42**, 813-845.

KROMMAN R.P. (1973) The energy value of feeds as affected by associative effects. *Proceedings 1ˢᵗ International Green Crop Drying Conference.*

KRYSL L.J., GALYEAN M.L., ESTELL R.E. and SOWELL B.F. (1988) Estimating digestibility and faecal output in lambs using internal and external markers. *Journal of Agricultural Science, Cambridge,* **111**, 19-25.

LABY R.H., GRAHAM C.A., EDWARDS S.R. and KAUTZNER B. (1984) A controlled release intra-ruminal device for the administration of faecal dry-matter markers to the grazing ruminant. *Canadian Journal of Animal Science,* **64** (Suppl.), 337-338.

LANGLANDS J.P. (1966) Studies on the nutritive value of the diet selected by grazing sheep. 1. Differences in composition between herbage consumed and material collected from the oesophageal fistulae. *Animal Production,* **9**, 253-259.

LANGLANDS J.P. (1967) Studies on the nutritive value of the diet selected by grazing sheep. III. A comparison of oesophageal fistula and faecal index techniques for the indirect estimation of digestibility. *Animal Production,* **9**, 325-331.

LANGLANDS J.P. and BENNETT L.L. (1973) Stoking intensity and pastoral production. II. Herbage intake of Merino sheep grazed at different stocking rates. *Journal of Agricultural Science, Cambridge,* **81**, 205-209.

LE DU Y.L.P. and PENNING P.D. (1982) Animal based techniques for estimating herbage intake. In: J.D. Leaver (ed). *Herbage Intake Handbook.* Published British Grassland Society, pp. 37-75.

LEITE E.R. and STUTH J.W. (1995) Faecal NIRS equations to assess diet quality of free-ranging goats. *Small Ruminant Research,* **15**, 223-230.

LE MANGEN J. (1971) Recent advances in the study of feeding. *Progress in Physiology and Psychology,* **4**, 203-253.

LESPERANCE A.L. and BOHMAN V.R. (1961) Apparatus for collecting excreta from grazing cattle. *Journal of Animal Science,* **20**, 503-505.

LYNCH J.J., HINCH J.N. and ADAMS D.B. (1992) The behaviour of sheep: biological principles and implications for production. CAB International, Wallingford, UK and CSIRO, East Melbourne, Australia. pp. 237.

LYONS R.K. and STUTH J.W. (1992) Faecal NIRS equations for predicting diet quality of free-ranging cattle. *Journal of Range Management,* **45**, 238-244.

MARAIS J.P., FIGENSCHOU P.L., ESCOTT-WATSON P.L. and WEBBER L.N. (1996) Administration in suspension-form of n-alkane external markers for dry matter intake and diet selection studies. *Journal of Agricultural Science, Cambridge,* **126**, 207-210.

MAYES R.W. (1998) New potential markers for determining diet composition. *Proceedings of the IXth European Intake Workshop.* Institute of Grassland and Environmental Research, North Wyke, U.K., November 1998, pp. 63-66.

MAYES R.W., DOVE H., CHEN X.B. and GUADA J.A. (1995) Advances in the use of faecal and urinary markers for measuring diet composition, herbage intake and nutrient utlisation in herbivores. In: Journet M., Grenet E., Farce M-H, Theriez M. and Dermaquilly C. (eds). *Recent Developments in the nutrition of herbivores.* INRA, Clermont-Ferrand (France) pp. 381-406.

MAYES R.W., DOVE H., LAMB C.S. and ELLIS K.J. (1991) Evaluation of an intra-ruminal device for controlled release of an alkane marker for intake estimation in sheep. *Proceedings of the 42ⁿᵈ meeting of the European Association of Animal Production,* Berlin, **1**, 457.

MAYES R.W., LAMB C.S. and COLGROVE P.M. (1986a) The use of dosed and herbage n-alkanes as markers for the determination of herbage intake. *Journal of Agricultural Science, Cambridge,* **107**, 161-170.

MAYES R.W., LAMB C.S. and COLGROVE P.M (1988) Digestion and metabolism of dosed even-chained and herbage odd-chained alkanes in sheep. *Proceedings 12th General Meeting of the European Grassland Federation,* 159-163.

MAYES R.W., WRIGHT I.A., LAMB C.S. and McBEAN A. (1986b) The use of long chain n-alkanes as markers for estimating intake and digestibility in cattle. *Animal Production,* **42**, 457.

MÉLIX C., PEYRAUD, J.L. and VÉRITÉ R. (1987) Utilisation de l'oxyde de chrome chez les vaches laitières pour la prevision des quantités de fèces émises. 1. Etude des variations du taux de recuperation et ses consequences sur l'estimation de la digestibilité et des quantités ingérées de rations d'herbe et d'ensilage de maïs. *Reproduction Nutrition Développment,* **27(1B)**, 215-216.

MICHELL A.R. (1977) An inexpensive metabolic harness for female sheep. *British Veterinary Journal,* **133**, 483-485.

MILNE J.A. and MAYES R.W. (1986) Supplementary feeding and herbage intake. *Hill Farming Research Organistaion Biennial Report 1984-85,* pp. 115-119.

MILNE J.A., MAXWELL T.J. and SOUTER W. (1981) Effect of supplementary feeding and herbage mass on intake and performance of grazing ewes in early lactation. *Animal Production,* **32**, 185-195.

MINSON D.J. and McLEOD M.N. (1972) The *in vitro* technique: Its modification for estimating digestibility of large numbers of tropical pasture samples. *Technical Paper No. 8,* Division of Tropical Pastures, CSIRO, Australia.

MINSON D.J. and RAYMOND W.F. (1958) Sources of error in the use of faecal index relationships. *Experiments in Progress, 10, 1956-57,* Published Grassland Research Institute, Hurley, pp. 92-96.

MINSON D.J., TAYLOR J.C., ALDER F.E., RAYMOND W.F., RUDMAN J.E., LINE C. and HEAD M.J. (1960) A method for identifying the faeces produced by individual cattle or groups of cattle grazing together. *Journal of the British Grassland Society,* **15**, 86-88.

MOLLE G., DECANDIA M. and DOVE H. (1998) A comparison between different procedures for dosing n-alkanes to sheep. *Proceedings of the IXth European Intake Workshop.* Institute of Grassland and Environmental Research, North Wyke, U.K., November 1998, pp. 53-57.

MORGAN J.B. and GOMEZ P.O. (1977) The production of chromic oxide paper pellets for use with young grazing cattle. *Journal of the British Grassland Society,* **32**, 49-50.

MURRAY I. (1993) Forage Analysis by Near Infra-red Spectroscopy. In: Davies A., Baker R.D., Grant S.A. and Laidlaw A.S. (eds). *Sward Measurement Handbook (2nd edition)* British Grassland Society, Reading U.K. pp 285-312.

NEWMAN J.A., CRIBARI-NETO F. and JENSEN M.J. (1998) The sensitivity of n-alkane analysis to measurement error: implications for use in the study of diet composition. *Journal of Agricultural Science, Cambridge,* **131**, 465-476.

NEWMAN J.A., PENNING P.D., PARSONS A.J., HARVEY A. and ORR R.J. (1994) Fasting affects intake behaviour and diet preference of grazing sheep. *Animal Behaviour,* **47**, 185-193.

NEWMAN J.A., THOMPSON W.A., PENNING P.D. and MAYES R.W. (1995) Least-squares estimation of diet composition from n-alkanes in herbage and faeces using matrix mathematics. *Australian Journal of Agricultural Research,* **46**, 793-805.

NOCEK J.E. (1988) *In situ* and other methods to estimate ruminal protein and energy digestibility: A review. *Journal of Dairy Science,* **71**, 2051-2069.

NORBURY G.L. and SANSOM G.D. (1992) Problems of measuring diet selection of terrestrial, mammalian herbivores. *Australian Journal of Ecology,* **17**, 1-7.

NUTHALL R., HUCKLE C.A. and GIBB M.J. (1994) Factors affecting the rate of insensible weight loss in Dairy Cattle. *Fourth BGS Research Conference,* British Grassland Society, September 1994, pp. 159-160.

OLIVÁN M., ORSORO K. and MARTINEZ K. (1994) Effect of temperature on alkane extraction from faeces and pasture. *45th Meeting of the European Association of Animal Production, Edinburgh,* pp. 184.

OMED H.M., AXFORD R.F.E., CHAMBERLAIN A.G. and GIVENS D.I. (1989) A comparison of three laboratory techniques for the estimation of the digestibility of feedstuffs for ruminants. *Journal of Agricultural Science, Cambridge,* **113**, 35-39.

ORR R.J., PENNING P.D., HARVEY A. and CHAMPION R.A. (1997) Diurnal patterns of intake rate by sheep grazing monocultures of grass or white clover. *Applied Animal Behaviour Science,* **52**, 65-77.

ORR R.J., RUTTER S.M., PENNING P.D. and ROOK A.J. (2001a) Matching grass supply to grazing patterns for dairy cows. *Grass and Forage Science,* **56**, 352-361.

ORR R.J., PENNING P.D., RUTTER S.M., CHAMPION R.A., HARVEY A. and ROOK A.J. (2001b) Intake rate during meals and meal duration for sheep in different hunger states, grazing grass or white-clover swards. *Applied Animal Behaviour Science,* **75**, 33-45.

PARKER W.J., MORRIS S.T., GARRICK D.J., VINCENT G.L. and McCUTCHEON S.N. (1990) Intraruminal chromium controlled release capsules for measuring herbage intake in ruminants - a review. *Proceedings New Zealand Society of Animal Production,* **50**, 437-442.

PARSONS, A. J. (1984) Guidelines for management of continuously grazed swards. *Grass Farmer,* **17**, 5-9

PARSONS A.J., NEWMAN J.A., PENNING P.D., HARVEY A. and ORR R.J. (1994) Diet preference of sheep: effects of recent diet, physiological state and species abundance. *Journal of Animal Ecology,* **63**, 465-478.

PENNING P.D. and GIBB M.J. (1979) The effect of milk intake on the intake of cut and grazed herbage by lambs. *Animal Production,* **29**, 53-67.

PENNING P.D. and HOOPER G.E. (1985) An evaluation of the use of short-term weight changes in grazing sheep for estimating herbage intake. *Grass and Forage Science,* **40**, 79-84.

PENNING P.D. and JOHNSON R.H. (1983a) The use of internal markers to estimate herbage digestibility and intake. 1 Potentially indigestible cellulose and acid insoluble ash. *Journal Agricultural Science, Cambridge,* **100**, 127-131.

PENNING P.D. and JOHNSON R.H. (1983b) The use of internal markers to estimate herbage digestibility and intake. 2 Indigestible acid detergent fibre. *Journal Agricultural Science, Cambridge,* **100**, 133-138.

PENNING P.D., ORR R.J. and TREACHER T.T. (1988) Responses of lactating ewes, offered fresh herbage indoors and when grazing, to supplements containing differing protein concentrations. *Animal Production,* **46**, 403-415.

PENNING P.D., PARSONS A.J., HOOPER G.E. and ORR R.J. (1994) Intake and behaviour responses by sheep to changes in sward characteristics under rotational grazing. *Grass and Forage Science,* **49**, 476-486.

PENNING P.D., PARSONS A.J., ORR R.J. (1991) Intake and behaviour responses by sheep to changes in sward characteristics under continuous stocking. *Grass and Forage Science,* **46**, 15-28.

PEYRAUD J.L. (1998) Techniques for measuring faecal flow, digestibility and intake of herbage in grazing ruminants. *Proceedings of the IXth European Intake Workshop.* Institute of Grassland and Environmental Research, North Wyke, U.K., November 1998, pp. 39-43.

PEYRAUD J.L., DELABY L and DELAGARDE (1998) Effet de l'apport de concentre énergétique et des quantités d'herbe offerte sur l'ingestion des vaches laitières au pâturage. *Rencontres Recherches Ruminants,* **5**, 217-221.

PIASENTIER E., BOVOLENTA S., MALOSSINI F. and SUSMEL P. (1995) Comparison of n-alkanes or chromium oxide methods for estimation of herbage intake by sheep. *Small Ruminant Research,* **18**, 27-32.

PLAYNE M.J. (1978), Differences between cattle and sheep in their digestion and relative intake of mature tropical grass hay. *Animal Feed Science and Technology,* **3**, 41-49.

RAYMOND W.F. and MINSON D.J. (1955) The use of chromic oxide for estimating the faecal production of grazing animals. *Journal of the British Grassland Society,* **10**, 282-296.

ROMNEY D.L., SENDALO D.S.C., OWEN E., MTENGA L.A., PENNING P.D. and MAYES R.W. (1996) Effects of tethering management on feed intake and behaviour of Tanzanian goats. *Small Ruminant Research,* **19**, 113-120.

ROYAL W.M. (1968) Equipment for the collection of faeces from sheep. *Proccedings of the Australian Society of Animal Production,* **7**, 450-454.

ROOK A.J. and HUCKLE C.A. (1997) Activity bout criteria for grazing cows. *Applied Animal Behaviour Science,* **54**, 89-96.

ROOK A.J., HUCKLE C.A. and PENNING P.D. (1994) Effects of sward height and concentrate supplementation on the ingestive behaviour of spring-calving dairy cows grazing grass-clover swards. *Applied Animal Behaviour Science,* **40**, 101-112.

SALT C.A., MAYES R.W., COLGROVE P.M. and LAMB C.S. (1994) The effects of season and diet consumption on the radiocaesium intake by sheep grazing heather moorland. *Journal of Applied Ecology,* **31**, 125-136.

SCHILD G. J. and HONIG H. (1975) Methodische Untersuchungen zur Bewertung von Grundfutter. 1. Teil: Schnellbestimmung des Trockenmassegehalts im Grundfutter. *Sonderheft der Bericht über Landwirtschaft,* **191**, 393-401.

SCHNEIDER B.H. and FLATT W.P. (1975) The evaluation of feeds through digestibility experiments. Publication *The University of Georgia Press.* Athens 30602 USA.

SIBBALD A.M, DAVIDSON G.C. and MAYES R.W. (2000) Effect of dosing regime on intake estimation using the n-alkane technique in sheep fed pelleted grass meal. *Journal of Science Food and Agriculture,* **80**, 1206-1210.

STAKELUM G. and DILLON (1990) Dosed and herbage alkanes as feed intake predictors with dairy cows: the effect of feeding level and frequency of perennial ryegrass. *Proceedings VII European Grazing Workshop,* Wageningen, The Netherlands, October 1990.

SUSMEL P., STEFANON B., SPANGEHERO M. and MILLS C.R. (1996) Ability of mathematical models to predict faecal output with a pulse dose indigestible marker. *British Journal of Nutrition,* **75**, 521-532.

TAYLER J.C. and DERIAZ R.E. (1963) The use of rumen fistulated steers in the direct determination of nutritive value of ingested herbage in grazing experiments. *Journal of the British Grassland Society,* **18**, 29-38.

TERRY R.A., MUNDELL D.C. and OSBOURN D.F. (1978) Comparison of two *in vitro* procedures using rumen liquor-pepsin or pepsin-cellulase for prediction of forage digestibility. *Journal British Grassland Society,* **33**, 13-18.

THERIEZ M. and DERMAQUILLY C. (eds). *Recent Developments in the nutrition of herbivores.* INRA, Clermont-Ferrand (France) pp. 381-406.

TILLEY M.A. and TERRY R.A. (1963) A two stage technique for the *in vitro* digestion of forage crops. *Journal of the British Grassland Society,* **18**, 104-111.

TOLKAMP. B.J., ALLCROFT D.J., AUSTIN E.J., NIELSEN B.L. and KYRIAZAKIS I. (1998) Satiety splits behaviour into bouts. *Journal of Theoretical Biology,* **194**, 235-250.

TORELL D.T. (1954) An oesophageal fistula for animal nutrition studies. *Journal of Animal Science,* **13**, 878-884.

TROELSEN J.E. (1963) Note on chromic oxide paper pellets for administration to ruminants. *Canadian Journal of Animal Science,* **43**, 389-390.

TROELSEN J.E. (1966) Pelleting of chromic oxide for administration to cattle and sheep. *Canadian Journal of Animal Science,* **46**, 226-227.

UDÉN P., COLUCCI P.E. and VAN SOEST P.J. (1980) Investigation of chromium, cerium and cobalt as markers in digesta. Rate of passage studies. *Journal of Science Food and Agriculture,* **31**, 625-632.

VALDERRABANO J. (1979) Techniques of measuring intake by grazing sheep. *M. Phil. Thesis, University of Reading.* pp. 145.

VAN DYNE G.M. and TORELL D.T. (1964) Development and use of oesophageal fistula: a review. *Journal of Range Management,* **17**, 7-19.

VAN SOEST P.J. (1994) Nutritional ecology of the ruminant, 2nd Edition, Cornell University Press, Ithaca, New York and London, pp 476.

VULICH S.A. and HANRAHAN J.P. (1995) Faecal sampling for the estimation of herbage intake using n-alkanes - evaluation of sampling pooling and the use of rectal grab samples. *Journal of Agricultural Science,* **124**, 79-86.

VULICH S.A., HANRAHAN J.P. and O'RIORDAN E.G. (1993) Pasture sampling for the estimation of herbage intake using n-alkanes: Evaluation of alternative sampling procedures. *Irish Journal of Agriculture and Food Research,* **32**, 1-11.

VULICH S.A., HANRAHAN J.P. and CROWLEY (1995) Modification of the analytical procedures for determination of herbage and faecal n-alkanes used in the estimation of herbage intake. *Journal of Agricultural Science, Cambridge,* **124**, 71-77.

VULICH S.A., O'RIORDAN E.G. and HANRAHAN J.P. (1991) Use of n-alkanes for the estimation of herbage intake in sheep: accuracy and precision of estimates. *Journal of Agricultural Science, Cambridge,* **116**, 319-323.

WEISS W.P. (1994) Estimation of digestibility of forages by laboratory methods. In: Fahey J.C. (ed). *Forage quality, evaluation and utilization.* Wisconsin, U.S.A. American Society of Agronomy, Inc., pp. 644-681.

WHITE P.F., TREACHER T.T., TERMANININ A. and RIAHAWI S. (1997) The accuracy of using the ratio of nitrogen to acid detergent fibre in faeces to partition nitrogen between faeces and urine in total excreta collections from ewes. *Grass and Forage Science,* **52**, 122-124.

WILKINS R.J. (1969) The potential digestibility of cellulose in forage and faeces. *Journal of Agricultural Science, Cambridge,* **73**, 57-64.

WINSLOW C.E.A. and HERRINGTON L.P.(1949) Temperature and human life. *Princeton University Press,* Princeton, New Jersey, USA, pp. 272.

# CHAPTER 4

# ESTIMATING HERBAGE INTAKE FROM ANIMAL PERFORMANCE

**R D Baker**

## 4.1 INTRODUCTION

The use of animal data as a basis for calculating the herbage intake of grazing livestock is attractive because in its simplest form only the weighing of animals and animal products, record keeping and calculations are involved. Thus the method offers an alternative to the more demanding techniques based upon pasture measurements or upon faecal output/digestibility relationships. This approach may be the only one available in some situations where labour or laboratory facilities are limiting. The terminology and symbols used in this chapter are as defined by AFRC (1993) and are defined in the glossary (4.10).

Herbage intake (HI kg DM) is calculated from the metabolisable energy (MJ) required for maintenance and production of the animals involved ($M_{mp}$) and that total requirement equated with herbage of a given metabolisable energy concentration (M/D, MJ).

Thus:

$$HI = \frac{M_{mp}}{M/D} \qquad (4.1)$$

The precision of the estimate is therefore entirely dependent on the adequacy of energy standards and the ability to measure animal production accurately. As with all techniques for measuring herbage intake there are errors and biases in the calculated figures arising from the assumptions made. The potential sources of variation are considered in the following sections.

## 4.2 EFFICIENCY OF UTILISATION OF ME

The efficiency with which energy is utilised varies with both the function it supports in the animal and the energy content in the feed. Equations for the former, as defined by ARC (1980), are given in section 4.8.

Small biases and errors may occur in calculating herbage intake depending on the way in which herbage energy is established. The metabolisability of the diet as M/D was adopted by ARC (1965) because of a paucity of information on the Gross Energy (GE) of feeds. However greater precision is obtained by using the metabolisability of the GE of a feed at maintenance ($q_m$) as a proportion of the ME in the GE. Therefore:

$$q_m = ME/GE \qquad (4.2)$$

Greatest precision is obtained by using actual measurements of GE rather than a mean value of 18.4 MJ kg DM$^{-1}$. In most circumstances this will not be possible and as GE could vary by ±0.5 of a unit some under or over estimation may occur.

## 4.3 LEVEL OF FEEDING EFFECTS

At higher levels of feeding the ME available to an animal is significantly reduced due to increased outflow rates from the rumen and reduced retention time in the rumen. Consequently, MacHardy (1965) suggested scaling by fasting metabolism to take account of this effect. Whilst animal production level became an integral part of calculations for establishing the requirements of growing beef cattle and sheep (MAFF, 1975) it was only indirectly covered for dairy cows by the inclusion of safety margins. The decline is estimated by ARC (1980) as 1.8% per unit increase in feeding level (L) above maintenance. The correction factor for lactating ruminants is calculated as:

$$C_L = 1 - 0.018 (L-1) \qquad (4.3)$$

where L is multiples of maintenance ME requirement.

Failure to take the effect of level of feeding into account means that herbage intake will be under estimated to the same extent as the reduction in the yield of metabolisable energy.

## 4.4    MEASURES OF USABLE ENERGY

There is no universal system of expressing the energy requirements of livestock or of evaluating the energy content of feeds. Whilst net energy now provides the basis for all systems, energy values may be expressed as Digestible Energy (DE), Metabolisable Energy (ME) or Net Energy (NE), as Total Digestible Nutrients (TDN) or as Feed Units. The quest to improve existing systems and to develop new ones is ongoing. Consequently there are several systems in operation and the choice of system can substantially affect the estimate under some circumstances.

All systems distinguish between dairy cows and growing/fattening cattle with the exception of the one adopted by the former German Democratic Republic (Schiemann *et al.,* 1971). There are, however, differences between systems because there is a lack of agreement on animal requirements, particularly for growing animals, and on the means of predicting the energy content of feeds. There has also been a greater acceptance of simplification and the use of average figures in some schemes than others. For detailed descriptions the reader should refer to the National Research Council publications (1978; 1982; 1984; 1989) for the American TDN, DE, ME, and NE systems, to MAFF (1975), ARC (1980), AFRC (1990) and AFRC (1993) for the development of the British ME system and to Van Es (1978); Vermorel (1978), INRA (1978) and Vermorel *et al.* (1987); Bickel and Landis (1978); and Bronsch *et al.* (1979) for the NE systems adopted in Holland, France, Switzerland and West Germany respectively. More recently a modification to the American system has been proposed as the Cornell Net Carbohydrate and Protein System (CNCPS), (Russell *et al.* (1992), Sniffen *et al.* (1992) and Fox *et al.* (1992).

## 4.5 ENERGY REQUIREMENTS

### 4.5.1 Maintenance

It is generally accepted that maintenance requirements are proportional to some power of live weight and that they also depend on the extent of an animals activity. The lack of agreement on whether the exponent should be live weight $W^{0.67}$, $W^{0.73}$ or $W^{0.75}$ and on the additional energy requirements for activity will lead to variations in the estimates of herbage intake. In some cases maintenance is regarded as equal to fasting metabolism whereas in others an activity allowance is added to allow for the energy expended for the voluntary muscular activity associated with normal feeding conditions. Distinctions are drawn between tied animals (which sometimes are equated with those kept in calorimeters), loose housed animals and those grazing. Examples of the differences that arise for housed animals are given in Table 4.1.

The extent to which activity allowances should be increased for grazing animals depends upon the topography and pasture conditions at each location. ARC (1965) concluded that estimates made of the energy cost of grazing do not warrant the inclusion of any additional allowance for the act of grazing but they did acknowledge the increased needs arising from extra walking, climbing and standing. Using their

Table 4.1. *Requirements for maintenance expressed as net energy in relation to liveweight, (LW).*

| | Energy system | | | | | |
|---|---|---|---|---|---|---|
| | MAFF (1975) | NRC (1975-1978) | Van Es (1978) | Vermorel (1978) | Bickel and Landis (1978) | Bronsch et al. (1979) |
| Exponent of LW (e) | 0.73 | 0.75 | 0.75 | 0.75 | 0.75 | 0.75 |
| 600 kg cow activity increment | +10% | +10% | 0(or + 5%) | 0 (or + 10%) | 0 | 0 |
| Maintenance requirement MJ NE kg $^{-1}$LW$^e$ | 0.396 | 0.335 | 0.293 or (0.308)[1] | 0.293 or (0.322)[1] | 0.293 | 0.29 |
| Total requirement MJ NE day $^{-1}$ | 42.2 | 40.6 | 35.5 (37.4)[1] | 35.5 (39.1)[2] | 35.5 | 35.5 |
| 250 kg steer activity increment | 0 | 0 | +10% | +10% | +10% | 0 |
| Maintenance requirement MJ NE kg $^{-1}$LW$^e$ | 0.396 | 0.322 | 0.330 | 0.333 | 0.330 | 0.293 |
| Total requirement | 21.1 | 20.2 | 20.7 | 20.7 | 20.7 | 18.4 |
| 60kg ewe activity increment | +15% | N G | - | N G | - | - |
| Maintenance requirement MJ NE kg $^{-1}$LW$^e$ | 0.265 | 0.287[3] | - | 0.278[3] | - | - |
| Total requirement MJ NE day$^{-1}$ | 5.3 | 6.2 | - | 6.0 | - | - |

NG = not stated whether an activity increment is included

[1]Requirement increased by 5% for loose housed cattle over tied cattle

[2]Requirement increased by 10% for loose housed cattle over tied cattle

[3]Adjusted from ME with an efficiency of utilisation for maintenance of 0.70

figures the 10% activity allowance recommended would be sufficient for cattle walking 3 km daily.

AFRC (1990) recommended an increase in activity allowances based upon assumptions of the extent of horizontal (HM) and vertical movement (VM), of the duration of standing (S) and of the number of body positional changes (BPC) each day. Thus:

$$\text{Activity} = HM + VM + S + BPM \qquad (4.4)$$

The energy costs of horizontal movement by cattle and sheep have been stated as 2.0 and 2.6 J per kg LW per metre respectively (ARC 1980). For vertical movement 28J per kg LW per metre has been recommended for both cattle and sheep. The effect of a 400 kg bullock travelling 3 km and ascending 200 m daily is to increase energy expenditure by 4.64 MJ or 15% more than for fasting metabolism. The increase for a 50 kg ewe would be 0.67 MJ or a 16% increase. No specific recommendation is made by MAFF (1975) but NRC (1978) recommended that maintenance for grazing dairy cows be increased by 3% for each km walked. They suggest that the needs are 10% higher for cows grazing lush pasture and 20% for those grazing sparse pasture. The importance of the exercise factor in maintenance has been discussed by Logan and Pigden (1969) and the estimates made for the maintenance of sheep kept indoors and outdoors have been summarised by Tissier et al. (1978). The average value for housed sheep was 0.397 MJ of ME per $W^{0.75}$ and this value has been adopted in the French system. Estimates for grazing sheep have ranged from 0.402-0.910 MJ ME with a mean value of 0.596 MJ per $W^{0.75}$, a 50% increase over housed sheep. All the latter estimates were made in New Zealand and Australia and their exact relevance to European conditions is uncertain.

Assessing the magnitude of the activity increment is the most important difficulty in estimating the maintenance requirements of grazing livestock. However, small differences may arise from, a) fluctuations in gut fill which affect estimates of live weight, and b) the effects of adverse weather conditions.

Increases of up to 8% in total feed allowances have been recommended (NRC, 1978) for cows kept under severe winter conditions in the northern states of America. Precise estimates of maintenance energy requirements are generally not required for grazing livestock as controlled rationing of feed is not attempted. For this reason, and also because precise requirements are ill-defined, most of the energy systems adopted do not include guidance on the requirements of grazing animals. However, the evidence available indicates that 10-20% additional energy will be required by animals grazing small fields and paddocks but that substantially more will be required for those kept under hill and rangeland conditions.

### 4.5.2 Milk production

The net energy requirement for milk production is the energy value ($EV_L$, MJ $kg^{-1}$) of the milk secreted. This may be estimated from the fat [BF], protein [P] and lactose [La] content (g $kg^{-1}$) or from fat and solids not fat (SNF) contents (Tyrell and Reid 1965).

$$[EV_L] = 0.03840 [BF] + 0.02226[P] + 0.01992 [La] - 0.1081 \tag{4.5}$$
or
$$[EV_L] = 0.0386 [BF] + 0.0205 [SNF] - 0.236 \tag{4.6}$$

In some systems it is customary to relate requirements to 4% fat corrected milk (FCM) whereas others tabulate requirements against fat content or against fat and solids not fat contents. Solids corrected milk (SCM) may also be used. FCM and SCM can be calculated from the equations:

$$FCM = 0.4 \text{ (weight of milk)} + 15 \text{ (weight of fat)} \tag{4.7}$$

$$SCM = \text{Milk yield (kg)} \times [EV_L] \text{ (MJ kg}^{-1}) / 3.1362 \text{ (MJ kg}^{-1}) \tag{4.8}$$

The denominator in Equation 4.8 is the approximate energy value of 1 kg of 4% FCM. The actual values for FCM adopted by different countries vary in relation to what is considered the average milk produced. The range of values adopted amounts to nearly 9% between NRC and the Netherlands and is shown in Table 4.2.

Table 4.2. Energy values of 4% Fat Corrected Milk (MJ kg$^{-1}$).

| | Energy system | | | | | |
|---|---|---|---|---|---|---|
| | MAFF (1975) | NRC (1978) | Van Es (1978) | Vermorel (1978) | Bickel and Landis (1978) | Bronsch et al. (1979) |
| Energy value (MJ/KG) | 3.10 | 3.31 | 3.05 | 3.14 | 3.14 | 3.17 |

The requirements for net energy for the milk production of ewes is only stated in the British and French systems. A value of 4.6 MJ kg$^{-1}$ was adopted by the British (MAFF 1975) and is also recommended by the French during the first month of lactation. During the second month a value of 4.4MJ is used. An alternative approach for ewes has been given by Brett et al. (1972) who estimated energy value (MJ kg$^{-1}$) by regression on the days (d) after lambing, where BF is g kg$^{-1}$.

$$[EV_L] = 0.0328[BF] + 0.025d + 2.203 \tag{4.9}$$

The revised British system now recommends that a weighted mean value of 70g kg$^{-1}$ is used when information on butterfat content is unavailable, giving a range of values for [EV$_l$] rising from 4.5 - 4.7 MJ kg$^{-1}$ milk over the ewe's lactation.
Estimates of milk yield of ewes are given in Table 4.3

*Table 4.3. Estimates of ewe milk yields (kg/d) by month of lactation.(AFRC, 1990).*

| Litter size | Type of ewe | Month of lactation | | |
|---|---|---|---|---|
| | | 1 | 2 | 3 |
| One Lamb | Hill | 1.25 | 1.05 | 0.70 |
| | Lowland | 2.10 | 1.70 | 1.05 |
| Two Lambs | Hill | 1.90 | 1.60 | 1.10 |
| | Lowland | 3.00 | 2.25 | 1.50 |

4.5.3 Pregnancy

Pregnant animals have a higher basal metabolism and require additional energy to cover this need and for the synthesis of foetal and associated tissues and their maintenance. The foetus, foetal membranes, fluids and the uterus grow at an exponential rate. Thus some 64% (Becker *et al.*, 1950) of the total foetus and the accompanying tissue and fluids were laid down in Jersey cows in the last 2 months of pregnancy and 70% in Merino ewes carrying a single foetus over the same period (Langlands and Sutherland, 1968). For the most part the extra requirements for pregnancy are ignored during the first 6 to 7 months of gestation for cattle and the first 90 days for sheep. However, ARC (1980) have published equations which permit the calculation of energy retention in the foetus and gravid uterus for cattle and sheep in relation to stage of gestation and the expected birth weight. For cows the energy requirement will have already increased by about 13% after 6 months but only 3-5% for ewes after 90 days.

Precise requirements for pregnancy are not stated in all feeding systems and, as for maintenance and lactation, there is no universal agreement on them. For cows, the requirement for the seventh month of pregnancy is generally stated as the equivalent of 2 kg FCM, but ranges from 4 to 8 kg in the ninth month depending on the feeding standards adopted. Variations also exist in the standards adopted for ewes. For example, the MAFF and French standards suggest that the energy requirement during the last six weeks is about 1.3 and 1.5 x maintenance for single and twin bearing 60 kg ewes whereas NRC standards are 1.5 and 2.0 x maintenance. New standards suggested by ARC (1980) are similar to the latter at 1.5 and 1.8 x maintenance.

4.5.4 Liveweight gain or loss

The energy requirements for liveweight gain increase with the growth of young animals but remain relatively constant for mature adults. They are also influenced markedly by the rate of gain or animal production level (APL) and the energy concentration of the food. The current feeding standards are mainly based on the Net Energy system, which was developed from the principles established by MacHardy

(1966) and worked out in detail by Harkins *et al.* (1974). This approach enables tables to be constructed which allow the net energy values ($NE_{mp}$) to be obtained if the animal production level (n times maintenance) and the energy value of the foods are known.

Although most systems for expressing requirements have a common basis there are still substantial differences in the values adopted. These relate to both differences in maintenance and production requirements. For example, MAFF (1975) recognised that the efficiency of utilisation of ME for maintenance ($k_m$) varies with the energy concentration of the diet, but because dietary extremes are found infrequently, they adopted single values for cattle and sheep of 0.72 and 0.70 respectively. The British system now uses a variable $k_m$ with values of 0.65 - 0.76 over the range of dietary energy concentrations of 8-14 M/D. This compares with ranges of 0.68 - 0.75 and 0.58 - 0.69 for the Dutch and American systems. Thus, although the net energy systems are almost identical, when expressed as ME for maintenance of grazing cattle consuming grass with an M/D of 11, the calculated requirement by NRC is 13% higher.

The daily metabolisable energy requirement is computed from the energy value of the gain and efficiency of ME utilisation for gain ($k_f$). As before, the $k_f$ values are related to the energy concentrations of the foods and those adopted by NRC (1984) are about 10% units lower than those adopted in Europe.

A more serious potential source of error in attempting to estimate herbage intake from records of liveweight gain arises when feeding standards do not take into account the effect of breed, sex and previous nutrition on the quantity of energy deposited per kg liveweight. Estimates for animals of the same live weight and growing at the same rate vary by anything up to 100% (Van Es, 1978). Thus reasonably accurate estimates of herbage intake will be possible only when the energy requirements used in the calculations reflect the breed and sex of the animals used. There are varying degrees of sophistication used in the approaches adopted. The French, ARC (1980) and AFRC (1993) take account of differences between bulls, steers and heifers, as well as the rate of maturity of breeds. In contrast the MAFF (1975) gives general tables applicable to all cattle. The same considerations apply in estimating the herbage intake of sheep but as with cattle a knowledge of the energy values of the liveweight gain is necessary before they can be taken into account.

Animals, particularly those lactating, may also go through periods of liveweight gain or loss. The average value of body tissue energy for cows has been taken as 20MJ (MAFF, 1975), 23.85 MJ (ARC, 1980), 19MJ (AFRC, 1993), 21MJ (Van Es, 1978) or 25MJ per kg live weight (NRC; Vermorel, 1978). ARC (1980) specifies that mobilised body reserves can be used with an efficiency of 0.84 and that its equivalence in dietary ME can be obtained by dividing by the feed $k_l$ (0.62) for lactation. Thus the net energy available from liveweight loss is:

$$NE = [EV_g] \times 0.84 \tag{4.10}$$

The equivalence in dietary energy is therefore:

$$ME = [EV_g] \times 0.84/ 0.62 \tag{4.11}$$

The current standards in Britain (AFRC, 1993) indicate for cattle that the NE (MJ) from liveweight loss is 15.96 kg$^{-1}$ and the dietary equivalence in ME is 25.74 kg$^{-1}$.

For sheep ARC (1980) recommended that the empty-body weight gain should be taken as 26 MJ kg$^{-1}$ so correcting by 1.09 to convert to liveweight gain or loss:

[EV$_g$] in lactating ewes = 23.85 MJ day$^{-1}$
and
NE from liveweight loss = 20.00 MJ day$^{-1}$

Thus the equivalence of liveweight loss in dietary energy is 32.3 MJ kg$^{-1}$.

## 4.6 THE ENERGY VALUE OF HERBAGE

Before herbage intake can be calculated from the energy requirements of animals an assessment of the energy value of the herbage is necessary. In some cases suitable values chosen from tables will be adequate. When greater precision is required it will be necessary to obtain samples of the herbage being eaten and to subject them to chemical analysis. Samples of herbage may be obtained by the use of oesophageal fistulated animals but if these are not available some other method of estimating the composition of the diet will be more appropriate. Normally samples would be collected by hand, taking care to ensure that they are representative of the herbage being selected (see Chapter 3).

The energy value of forages have been determined directly from controlled feeding trials to establish digestibility or Total Digestible Nutrients; from gross energy determinations on feeds and faeces to determine Metabolisable Energy (having assumed a loss of methane energy and either assumed or measured a loss of urine energy); or from calorimetric studies to extend the evaluation to Net Energy by direct determinations of methane output and heat production. From the information gathered on feeds many prediction equations have been developed linking digestibility and chemical composition to the ME values of feeds. The equations adopted reflect the type of information available within a country and the choice of energy system.

One of the most comprehensive sets of data on fresh forages is given by Terry *et al.* (1973) who related digestible energy [DE] to the contents (g kg$^{-1}$ DM) of the crude protein [CP] and the digestible organic matter in the dry matter [DOMD] by the equation:

[DE] = 0.1233 CP + 0.1705 DOMD + 0.285 MJ kg$^{-1}$ DM
and
ME assumed = 0.815 x [DE]                                                     (4.12)

Other equations were, until recently, based mainly on either total or digestible contents of crude protein, crude fat (CL), crude fibre (CF) and N-free extract (NFE). It is now more common to predict ME directly from either modified acid detergent fibre determinations of DOMD made using the in vitro technique (IVD) of Tilley and Terry (1963) or that of Dowman and Collins (1982) using neutral detergent cellulase (NCD). The following equations have been derived (Givens *et al.*, 1990):

$$ME\ (MJ\ kg^{-1}\ DM) = 16.20 - 0.0185\ [MADF]\ (g\ kg^{-1}\ DM) \tag{4.13}$$

$$= 3.24 + 0.0111\ [NCD]\ (g\ kg^{-1}\ DM) \tag{4.14}$$

$$= -0.46 + 0.0170\ [IVD]\ (g\ kg^{-1}\ DM) \tag{4.15}$$

The calculated intake of herbage will vary depending on which equation is used to predict energy value. Besides differences in the coefficient established, the need for separate constants to deal with differences between the value of forage for cattle and sheep is recognised in some equations and adjustments for level of feeding may also be incorporated. A comparison of the "energy potential" of feeds is given in Table 4.4 for two fresh grasses given by MAFF (1975).

Table 4.4. Estimated metabolisable energy value of fresh permanent pasture grass (MJ kg$^{-1}$ DM).

| | Prediction equation | | | | | | |
|---|---|---|---|---|---|---|---|
| | *MAFF* (1975) | Terry *et al.* (1973) | NRC (1969) | Van Es (1978) | Vermorel (1978) | Bickel and Landis (1978) | Bronsch *et al.* (1978) |
| Pasture grass closely grazed non-rotational | 12.1 | 13.3 | 12.0 | 12.0(C) 12.1(S) | 12.0(C) 12.1(S) | 12.0 | 12.0(C) 12.4(S) |
| Rotational with monthly intervals | 11.2 | 12.0 | 11.3 | 11.1(C) 11.2(S) | 11.2(C) 11.3(S) | 10.9 | 11.1(C) 11.3(S) |

(C) = cattle, (S) = sheep

Based upon closely grazed, pasture grass having CP, CL, CF and NFE contents of 265, 55, 130 and 455 g kg $^{-1}$DM and digestible contents of 225, 35, 105 and 387 g respectively and grass grazed rotationally having contents of 175, 50, 225 and 460 g kg$^{-1}$DM and digestible contents of 130, 25, 185 and 377 g respectively.

## 4.7 MEASURING ANIMAL PRODUCTION

The measurement of the milk production and milk quality of dairy cows can be done simply and accurately provided accepted procedures are followed. For example, recording the milk yield and taking aliquot samples for milk analysis at each milking on 1-2 days each week. However, for beef cows and ewes the task is more difficult. There are four main approaches to the problem of milk yield estimation and the reader should refer to Corbett (1978) and Coates and Penning (2000) for a general consideration of the different approaches. They are:

1. Weighing of offspring before and after a number of consecutive sucklings.
2. Measurement of milk secretion rate over 4-8 hours.
3. Estimation from previously established equations between liveweight gain and milk composition.
4. Estimations made from water turnover in the offspring.

Further information on the relative merits of suckling and machine milking techniques is available (Le Du *et al.*, 1979; Doney *et al.*, 1979; Somerville and Lowman, 1980; Coates and Penning, 2000) and on the estimation of milk quality following removal of milk after oxytocin injections (Le Du *et al.*, 1978).

The accurate estimation of liveweight change is of major importance if good estimates of herbage intake are to be obtained. Errors and possible bias in the estimates readily arise from changes in gut fill and the replacement of fat by water in animals losing weight. A further problem arises because the composition of the gain will vary in relation to breed, sex, age and, in some circumstances, previous nutrition. Also, over short periods of time, recorded liveweight gains and losses can be quite meaningless even when there is strict control over gut fill changes. Therefore estimates of energy loss or storage tend to become more accurate the longer the recording period: usually periods of less than 4-6 weeks are unsatisfactory. The difficulties of making measurements of liveweight and body composition and the precautions necessary have also been outlined by Corbett (1978) and Coates and Penning (2000) who also make reference to the more detailed investigations on which recommendations are made.

A further complication arises from pregnant animals as it is necessary to distinguish between liveweight gains due to the foetus and accompanying tissues and fluids, and those that are a genuine change in the body tissue of the dam. This is of importance because the energy value of the liveweight increase arising from the gravid uterus of both cattle and sheep is less than 5 MJ $^{kg-1}$, until the last month of pregnancy. Equations to predict the liveweight changes associated with pregnancy and their energy contents have been published by ARC (1980) and calculated values for cattle and sheep carrying different foetal burdens are given in Tables 4.5 and 4.6 respectively.

## 4.8 STANDARDS FOR THE CALCULATION OF ENERGY OUTPUT AND HERBAGE INTAKE

The calculation of herbage intake can be undertaken from a detailed consideration of energy requirements for fasting metabolism, activity and production, from the efficiencies associated with each of these processes, and from herbage analysis. For such an exercise individual judgements must be made on how appropriate each source of data is to the circumstances for which a calculation is being made. The most up-to-date collations of information are NRC (1984, 1989) and AFRC (1990, 1993).

Table 4.5. Estimated daily weight changes for the gravid uterus of cattle at 4 weekly intervals from conception (kg).

| Days from conception | Total foetal weight at birth (kg) | | | |
|---|---|---|---|---|
| | 25 | 35 | 45 | 55 |
| 113-141 | 0.13 | 0.15 | 0.18 | 0.20 |
| 142.169 | 0.16 | 0.21 | 0.26 | 0.31 |
| 170.197 | 0.21 | 0.29 | 0.36 | 0.44 |
| 198-225 | 0.26 | 0.37 | 0.49 | 0.60 |
| 226-253 | 0.32 | 0.47 | 0.63 | 0.78 |
| 254-281 | 0.38 | 0.56 | 0.76 | 0.97 |

Derived from equation given by ARC (1980)

Table 4.6. Estimated daily weight changes for the gravid uterus of sheep at 4 weekly intervals from conception (g).

| Days from conception | Total foetal weight at birth (kg) | | | |
|---|---|---|---|---|
| | 4 | 6 | 8 | 10 |
| 63-91 | 30 | 46 | 57 | 69 |
| 92-119 | 59 | 92 | 115 | 144 |
| 120-147 | 96 | 140 | 205 | 260 |

Derived from equation given by ARC (1980)

Normally, recommended standards for energy requirements and the energy value of forages will be used and, as an example, those published by AFRC (1993) are given. Unlike earlier recommendations (MAFF, 1975) it is suggested that the energy requirement for fasting metabolism should be increased by an actual estimate of an animal's activity rather than by a percentage increase or a safety margin to cover this extra energy need. The recommended requirements (AFRC, 1993) for livestock are given below:

### 4.8.1 Dairy and Beef Cows

*ME allowance for maintenance (MJ day$^{-1}$)*

$$M_m = (F + A)/k_m \qquad\qquad (4.16)$$

where F = fasting metabolism, A = activity allowance (see below) and $k_m$ = efficiency of energy utilisation for maintenance

$$F(MJ\ d^{-1}) = C1\{0.53(W/1.08)^{0.67}\} \tag{4.17}$$

where C1 = 1.15 for bulls and 1.0 for other cattle
Factor 1.08 converts live weight (W) to fasted body weight.

*ME allowance for activity (MJ day$^{-1}$)*

$$A = (HM + VM + S + BPC)/1000 \tag{4.18}$$

Where:
HM = Horizontal Movement (2.0 J/ kgW/metre)
VM = Vertical Movement (28 J kg W/ metre)
S = Standing for 24 h (10J kJ/kgW/ day)
BPC = Body Position Change (260 J/ kgW)

A minimum activity for a grazing dairy cow is likely to be 3000m walked, 14 hours standing and 9 position changes (no vertical movement), giving:

$$A(kJ\ day^{-1}) = (6.00 + 5.83 + 2.34)W = 14.17W\ or$$

$$A(MJ\ day^{-1}) = 0.0142W$$

Activity for other classes of livestock will vary and appropriate figures should be substituted (AFRC, 1993).

*Efficiency of utilisation of ME for maintenance*

$$k_m = 0.35q_m + 0.503 \tag{4.19}$$

*ME allowance for milk production (MJ day$^{-1}$)*

$$E_1 = \frac{Energy\ secreted\ as\ milk\ EV_1\ x\ Yield\ (Y)}{Efficiency\ of\ energy\ utilsation\ for\ lactation\ (k_1)} \tag{4.20}$$

$$k_1 = 0.35q_m + 0.420 \tag{4.21}$$

*ME allowance for pregnancy (MJ day$^{-1}$)*

Energy retention in the gravid uterus and foetus assuming a 40kg calf birth weight is:

$$log_{10}(E_t) = 151.665 - 151.64e^{-0.0000576t} \tag{4.22}$$

where t is days from conception and $e = 2.718$ the base of the natural logarithm

$$E_c = 0.025W_c \, (E_t \times 0.0201e^{-0.0000576t}) \tag{4.23}$$

expressed as MJ day$^{-1}$ and $W_c$ is the calf birth weight in kg

$$k_c = 0.133 \text{ and is regarded as independent of M/D} \tag{4.24}$$

*ME allowance for liveweight gain*

$$EV_g = 19MJ \, kg^{-1} \text{ gain} \tag{4.25}$$

$$k_g = 0.95k_l \text{ for lactating cows} \tag{4.26}$$

$$k_f = 0.78qm + 0.006 \text{ for non-lactating growing ruminants} \tag{4.27}$$

*ME allowance for liveweight loss*

ARC (1980) specifies that mobilised body reserves are used with an efficiency of 0.84, therefore:

$$EV_g = 19 \times 0.84 = 16MJ \, kg^{-1} \text{ liveweight loss} \tag{4.28}$$

4.8.2 Growing cattle

*ME allowance for maintenance (MJ day$^{-1}$)*

As above for dairy and beef cows

ME allowances for growth (MJ day$^{-1}$)

$$[EV_g](MJ \, kg^{-1}) = \frac{C2 \, (4.1 + 0.0332W - 0.000009W^2)}{(1 - C3 \times 0.1475\Delta W)} \tag{4.29}$$

where C2 corrects for mature body size and sex of animal as below and $C3 = 1$ when plane of nutrition, $L>1$ and $= 0$ when $L<1$.

*Table 4.7. Values of the correction factor C2 for (EV$_g$) of liveweight gains in cattle by maturity and sex.*

| Maturity | Bulls | Castrates | Heifers |
|---|---|---|---|
| Early | 1.00 | 1.15 | 1.30 |
| Medium | 0.85 | 1.00 | 1.15 |
| Late | 0.70 | 0.85 | 1.00 |

## 4.8.3 Ewes

*ME allowance for maintenance (MJ day-1)*

$$F \text{ (MJ day}^{-1}) = 0.226(W/1.08)^{0.75} \tag{4.30}$$

*ME allowance for activity*

In general the energy allowances for sheep are the same as for cattle but a higher value is suggested for the horizontal movement of sheep of 2.6J kg $W^{-1}$ $m^{-1}$ (ARC 1980). A minimum activity for a grazing ewe is likely to be 1000m walked, standing for 12 hours and making 12 positional changes, giving:

$$A \text{ (kJ day}^{-1}) = (2.6 + 5.0 + 3.1)W = 10.7W \tag{4.31}$$
or
$$A( \text{ MJ day}^{-1}) = 0.0107W$$

Both distance walked and vertical movement would be considerably increased on sparser upland and hill pastures, with requirements more than doubled even on good quality range.

$$k_m = 0.35q_m + 0.503 \tag{4.32}$$

*ME allowance for milk production (MJ day$^{-1}$)*

The ME required for lactation, $M_l$, is calculated from:

$$M_l \text{ (MJ day}^{-1}) = (Y \times [EV_l])/k_l \tag{4.33}$$

The energy value of milk is:

$$EV_l \text{ (MJ kg}^{-1}) = 0.0328[BF] + 0.025d + 2.203 \tag{4.34}$$

Where d is the number of days after lambing, or alternatively:

$$EV_l \text{ (MJ kg}^{-1}) = 0.04194[BF] + 0.01585[P] + 0.2141[La ] \tag{4.35}$$

*ME allowance for pregnancy (MJ day$^{-1}$)*

The total energy content at time t ($E_t$, MJ) for the gravid uterus in ewes carrying a 4kg lamb:
$$\log_{10} (E_t) = 3.322 - 4.979^{-0.00643t} \tag{4.36}$$

AFRC (1990) then calculate the daily energy retention, $E_c$ as follows:

$$E_c, MJ/d = 0.25W_0 (E_t \times 0.07372e^{-0.00643t}) \tag{4.37}$$

(*where: t is number of days from conception and $W_o$ is the total weight of lambs at birth*)

$$k_c = 0.133 \text{ and is regarded as independent of M/D} \tag{4.38}$$

*ME allowance for liveweight gain*

$$[EV_g] = 23.85MJ \ kg^{-1} \ gain \tag{4.39}$$

$$k_g = 0.95k_1 \text{ for lactating ewes} = 0.95(0.35q_m + 0.420) \tag{4.40}$$

$$k_f = 0.78q_m + 0.006 \text{ for non-lactating ewes} \tag{4.41}$$

*ME allowance of liveweight loss*

$$[EV_g] = 20.0 \ MJ \ kg^{-1} \ liveweight \ loss \tag{4.42}$$

### 4.8.4 Growing sheep

*ME allowance for maintenance (MJ $d^{-1}$)*

$$\text{Up to 1 year of age } F = C1[0.25(W/1.08)^{0.75}] \tag{4.43}$$

$$\text{Over 1 year old } F = C1[0.23(W/1.08)^{0.75}] \tag{4.44}$$

where C1 = 1.15 for entire rams and 1.0 for females and castrates.

*ME allowance for activity (MJ/ $day^{-1}$)*

A minimum activity for a lamb is likely to be 500m walked, 10 hours standing and 12 positional changes, giving:

$$A \ (kgJ \ day^{-1}) = (1.3 + 4.16 + 3.1)W \tag{4.45}$$
or
$$0.086W \ MJ \ day^{-1}$$

$$k_m = 0.35q_m + 0.503 \tag{4.46}$$

*ME allowance for growth (MJ $d^{-1}$)*

The net energy retained in the animal's body is given by:

$$E_g = (\Delta W \times [EV_g]) \tag{4.47}$$

Three equations to predict the energy value (MJ d$^{-1}$) of the liveweight gain of growing lambs are:

Non-Merino males          $[EV_g] = 2.5 + 0.35W$          (4.48)

Castrates          $[EV_g] = 4.4 + 0.32W$          (4.49)

Females          $[EV_g] = 2.1 + 0.45W$          (4.50)

### 4.8.5 Deductions for supplementary feeds

*Milk.* In assessing the intake of suckling animals a deduction has to be made for the quantity of milk consumed. The energy values of average milk are for cows, 2.92 and for ewes, 4.60 MJ kg$^{-1}$. The apparent digestibility of milk is 98% and its ME = 97% of DE (Jagush, 1968). Consequently, the contribution of milk to energy requirements is:

Cows 0.98 x 0.97 x 2.92 = 2.78 MJ kg$^{-1}$ Milk          (4.51)

Ewes 0.98 x 0.97 x 4.60 = 4.37 MJ kg$^{-1}$ Milk          (4.52)

*Concentrate and forage supplements.* When supplementary feeds are given at pasture it is also necessary to make a deduction for their energy contribution. Feeds are credited with their stated ME value and it is assumed that there is no associative effect of feeds on their ME value. Supplementation will normally increase the level of feeding and in doing so may lead to a level of feeding effect on digestibility. The possibility of such an effect occurring was not acknowledged in the MAFF (1975) system and may lead to a bias in the estimate of herbage intake (see Chapter 3). In the following example calculations a level of feeding effect is included.

### 4.9 THE ACCURACY OF ESTIMATING HERBAGE INTAKE FROM ANIMAL PERFORMANCE

In the foregoing sections some of the variation in the energy standards adopted for the requirements of cattle and sheep, and for herbage quality have been highlighted. In some instances, these are of such a magnitude that the estimates of herbage intake from animal production data may be subject to large errors. In practice, however, the calculation is likely to be used most frequently to give an indirect estimate of the relative removal of herbage from a pasture by animals on one grazing treatment compared with one or more other treatments. The errors involved will tend to be systematic and in the same direction for each treatment. Therefore, relative differences will be fairly accurate. However, this is not the case when level of feeding effects are ignored.

Despite all the potential inaccuracies of the technique it has been found useful for obtaining relative measures of herbage intake, pasture productivity and the contribution of herbage to the diet of grazing animals: the last two providing measures of performance which have proved useful indicators of the efficiency with which grassland is utilised. The accuracy with which estimates of herbage intake can be made from measures of animal production cannot be stated precisely. However, for the most part, differences in the standards adopted for maintenance and production are unlikely to bias calculations by more than 10 per cent, a variability no greater than that of the alternative techniques. Under extensive and adverse grazing conditions a failure to estimate fully the increased energy requirements due to activity, could lead to significant under estimates of intake.

Provided animal production is assessed accurately the system outlined can give estimates of herbage intake which are acceptable for most purposes but it is not a method that can be recommended for critical studies. This is particularly so over short time periods because of the difficulties of accurately estimating changes in body weight which are not the result of changes in gut fill.

In the first edition of this book it was stated that as new information became available, the standards adopted would inevitably be modified to account of it but that the approach to the calculation of herbage intake would remain unaltered. This has been the case and in the following examples the standards currently recommended for Britain (AFRC, 1993) have been used rather than MAFF (1975) as previously.

## 4.9.1 Example calculations

Examples of herbage intake calculations from animal performance are given below for lactating dairy cows, steers, ewes and lambs.

4.9.1.1 *600 kg Cows giving 25 kg milk daily with no body weight change.* Assuming 3000km walked, 14 hours standing and 9 positional changes, milk composition (g kg$^{-1}$) BF 39.4, P 31.9, La 44.2 or (4.06, 3.29 and 4.55% litre$^{-1}$).

MJ day$^{-1}$

Fasting metabolism (Eq. 4.17)
$$0.53(600/1.08)^{0.67} = 36.58 \text{ MJ day}^{-1}$$

Activity (Eq. 4.18, 4.19)
$$(6.0 + 5.83 + 2.34)600/1000 = 8.50$$
$$k_m = 0.35 \times 0.61 + 0.503 = 0.7165$$

Maintenance = $(36.58 + 8.50)/0.7165 =$                                      62.92

Milk energy (Eq. 4.5, 4.21)
$$25(0.0384 \times 39.4 + 0.022 \times 31.9 + 0.0199 \times 44.2 - 0.108) = 74.89$$
$$k_l = 0.35 \times 0.61 + 0.42 = 0.6335$$

Milk requirement $74.66/0.6335 =$                                            118.23

Total requirement                                                           181.11

Level of feeding adjustment (Eq. 4.3)
    $1 + 0.018(2.87 - 1) = 1.034$

Total requirement from grass
    $(62.92 + 117.85) \times 1.034 =$                    187.31

Calculated herbage intake (kg DM day$^{-1}$) at grass M/D of 11.2 =         16.72

### 4.9.1.2 *600 kg Dry Cow at the 36th week of gestation (t=252 days)*. Gaining 0.5 kg$^{-1}$ in addition to the gain due to the conceptus and assuming 1000km walked, 14 hours standing and 9 positional changes with a calf of birth weight of 40 kg.

                                                        MJ day$^{-1}$

Maintenance (Eq. 4.17-19)
    As example 4.7.1.1 at                               59.57
    (adjusted for distance walked)

Gestation requirement (Eq. 4.18, 4.19, 4.20)

    $e^{-0.0000576 \ast t} = e^{-0.01452}$
    $[Antilog(151.665 - 151.64 e^{-0.01452})] \times$
    $(0.0201 e^{-0.01452}) \times (0.025 \times 40) = 3.22$

    $k_c = 0.133$
    $3.22/0.133 = 24.21$                                 24.21

Requirement for growth (Eq. 4.25, 4.27)
    $19 \times 0.5 = 9.5$

    $k_f = 0.78 \times 0.61 + 0.006 = 0.4818$
    $9.5/0.4818 =$                                       19.72
                                                        103.50

Level of feeding adjustment (Eq. 4.3)
    $1 + 0.018(1.73 - 1) = 1.013$

Total requirement from grass
    $1.013 \times 103.50 =$                              104.85

Calculated herbage intake (kg DM day$^{-1}$) at grass M/D of 11.2        9.36

### 4.9.1.3 *350 kg medium maturity steer.* Gaining 0.9 kg daily and receiving no additional feed, assuming 1000m walked, 12 hours standing and 6 positional changes.

                                                        MJ day$^{-1}$

Fasting metabolism requirement (Eq. 4.17)
    $0.53(350/1.08)^{0.67} = 25.49$

Activity requirement (Eq.4.18, 4.19)
    $(2.00 + 5.00 + 1.56)350/1000 = 3.0$
    $k_m = 0.35 \times 0.61 + 0.503 = 0.7165$

Maintenance requirement
    $(25.5 + 3.0)/0.7165 = 39.78$                                        39.78

Liveweight gain requirement (Eq. 4.27, 4.29)
    (Note C2 =1 (Table 4.6) and C3 =1)

$$[EV_g] \text{ (MJ/kg)} = \frac{4.1 + 0.0332 \times 350 - 0.000009 \times 350^2}{1 - (0.1475 \times 0.9)} = 16.86$$

    $EV_g$ adjusted for liveweight gain $= 16.86 \times 0.9 = 15.17$
    $k_g = 0.78 \times 0.61 + 0.006 = 0.4818$

    Requirement $= 15.17/0.4818 =$                                       31.49
                                                                         71.27

Level of feeding adjustment (Eq. 4.3)
    $1 + 0.018(1.79 - 1) = 1.014$

Total requirement from grass
    $1.014 \times 71.27 =$                                               72.28

Calculated herbage intake (kg DM day$^{-1}$) at grass M/D of 11.2 =      6.45

4.9.1.4 *A 60 kg ewe.* Giving 2kg milk daily and gaining 50 g day$^{-1}$ assuming 1000m walked, 12 hours standing and 12 positional changes daily, $[EV_1]$ milk 4.6.

                                                                         MJ day$^{-1}$

Requirement for fasting metabolism (Eq. 4.30)
    $0.226(60/1.08)^{0.75} = 4.599$

Requirement for activity (Eq. 4.4, 4.31,4.32)
    $(2.6 + 5.0 + 3.1)60/1000 = 0.642$
    $k_m = 0.35 \times 0.61 + 0.503 = 0.7165$

Requirement for maintenance
    $(4.599 + 0.642)/0.7165 =$                                           7.31

Requirement for liveweight gain (Eq. 4.39, 4.40)
    $23.85 \times 0.05 = 1.192$
    $k_g = (0.35 \times 0.61 + 0.420)0.95 = 0.6018$

Total requirement for liveweight gain $1.192/0.6018 =$                   1.98

Requirement for milk (Eq. 4.17, 4.30)
   $k_l = 0.35 \times 0.61 + 0.42 = 0.6335$
   $EV_l = 4.6 \times 2.0 = 9.2$

Total requirement for milk
   $9.2/0.6335 =$                                                14.52
                                                                 23.81

Level of feeding adjustment (Eq.4.3)
   $1 + 0.018(3.26 - 1) = 1.041$

Total energy from grass
   $23.81 \times 1.041 =$                                        24.79

Calculated herbage intake (kg day$^{-1}$) at grass M/D of 11.2          2.21

4.9.1.5 *A 30 kg castrate lamb*. Growing at 200 g day$^{-1}$ and receiving 750 g day$^{-1}$ of milk assuming 500m walked, 12 hours standing and 10 positional changes

MJ day$^{-1}$

Requirement for fasting metabolism (Eq.4.43)
   $0.25(30/1.08)^{0.75} = 3.025$

Requirement for activity (Eq.4.4, 4.45, 4.46)
   $(1.3 + 5.0 + 2.6) \times 30/1000 = 0.267$
   $k_m = 0.35 \times 0.61 + 0.503 = 0.7165$

Requirement for maintenance
   $(3.025 + 0.267)/0.7165 =$                                    4.59

Requirement for liveweight gain (Eq. 4.27, 4.47, 4.49)
   $k_f = 0.78 \times 0.61 + 0.006 = 0.4818$
   $EV_g = [4.4 + (0.32 \times 30)] \times 0.2 = 2.8$
   Requirement $= 2.8/0.4818 =$                                  5.81

Contribution of milk (Eq. 4.52)
   $4.37 \times 0.75 = 3.28$                                     -3.28
                                                                 7.12

Level of feeding adjustment (Eq. 4.3)
   $1 + 0.018(1.55 - 1.0) = 1.001$

Total energy from grass
   $1.001 \times 7.12 =$                                         7.13

Calculated herbage intake (kg day$^{-1}$) at grass M/D of 11.2 =        0.64

## 4.10 GLOSSARY OF TERMS USED

This glossary is derived from that given by AFRC (1993).

UPPERCASE LETTERS are used for energy and nutrient supply (per animal) per day, either g/d or MJ/d as appropriate.

The same symbols, enclosed in square brackets, e.g. [DE], are used for concentrations, g/kg or MJ/kg, except where existing usage dictates otherwise.

Lower case letters are used for rates, efficiencies and proportions, which are either expressed as decimals (not percentages), or with relevant units, e.g. g/MJ.

The units and abbreviations used for weight, time etc are in SI units.

Subscripts are used to differentiate between metabolic functions as follows:

| | |
|---|---|
| b | Basal metabolism |
| c | Concepta/gravid foetus/pregnancy |
| f | Liveweight gain |
| g | Gain/loss in liveweight in lactating animals |
| l | Lactation |
| m | Maintenance |
| o | Ovine |
| p | Production |
| t | Time in days |

| | |
|---|---|
| A | Activity allowance, J/kg/m or kJ/kg/d |
| B | Derived parameter in equation (14) to predict energy retention |
| [BF], B % | Butterfat content of milk, g/kg or % per litre |
| C | Concentrate DM fed, kg/d |
| Cl - C6 | Correction factors used in the calculation of the ME requirements |
| $C_L$ | Plane of nutrition correction factor in calculating ME requirements of lactating ruminants |
| CP, [CP] | Crude Protein, g/d in a diet or g/kgDM in a feed |
| DE, [DE] | Digestible Energy, MJ/d of a diet or MJ/kgDM in a feed |
| DMI, [DM] | Dry Matter, intake, kg/d, or content, g/kg in a feed |
| DOM, [DOMD] | Digestible Organic Matter, kg/d in a diet or g/kgDM in a feed |
| E, [E] | Net Energy, MJ/d or g/kg |
| $E_c$ | Net Energy retained in concepta, MJ/d |
| $E_f$ | Net Energy retained in growing animal, MJ/d |
| $E_g$ | Net Energy retained or lost in daily weight change in lactating ruminants, MJ/d |
| $E_l$ | Net Energy secreted as milk, MJ/d |

| | |
|---|---|
| $E_m$ | Net Energy for maintenance, MJ/d |
| $E_{mp}$ | Net Energy for maintenance and production, MJ/d |
| $E_t$ | Net Energy content of concepta at time t, MJ |
| $E_w$ | Net Energy retained as wool or goat fibre, MJ/d |
| EBW | Empty-body weight, kg |
| [EE] | Ether Extract (oil), in feed, g/kgDM |
| $[EV_g]$ | Energy Value of tissue lost or gained, MJ/kg |
| $[EV_l]$ | Energy Value of milk, MJ/kg |
| exp | Exponential function using base e |
| F | Fasting metabolism, MJ/(kg fasted weight)$^{0.67}$ |
| FE | Faeces energy, MJ/d |
| $F_p$ | Proportion of forage in the diet Dry Matter |
| GE, [GE] | Gross Energy of a diet, MJ/d or MJ/kgDM in a feed |
| HI | Herbage Intake kg DM/hd/d |
| I | Intake of dietary ME, MJ/d scaled by fasting metabolism, F |
| [IVD] | *in vitro* digestibility [DOMD], g/kgDM of a feed |
| k | Derived parameter in equation (15) to predict energy retention |
| $k_c$ | Efficiency of utilisation of ME for growth of the concepta |
| $k_f$ | Efficiency of utilisation of ME for weight gain |
| $k_g$ | Efficiency of utilisation of ME for weight change when lactating |
| $k_l$ | Efficiency of utilisation of ME for milk production |
| $k_m$ | Efficiency of utilisation of ME for maintenance |
| $k_t$ | Efficiency of utilisation of mobilised tissue for lactation |
| ln | Natural logarithm to base e |
| L | Level of feeding as a multiple of MJ of ME for maintenance |
| [La], La % | Lactose content of milk, g/kg or % per litre |
| LWG or $\Delta W$ | Liveweight gain or change, ± g or kg/d |
| $M_c$ | ME requirement for growth of concepta, MJ/d |
| $M_f$ | ME requirement for liveweight gain, MJ/d |
| $M_g$ | ME requirement for liveweight change when lactating, MJ/d |
| $M_l$ | ME requirement for milk production, MJ/d |
| $M_m$ | ME requirement for maintenance, MJ/d |
| $M_{mp}$ | ME requirement for maintenance and production, MJ/d |
| $M_w$ | ME requirement for wool or fibre growth, MJ/d |
| $M_E$ | Methane energy, MJ/d |
| [MADF] | Modified Acid Detergent Fibre in feed, g/kgDM |
| M/D | Metabolisable Energy, MJ/kgDM of a diet, see also [ME] for a feed or diet |
| ME, [ME] | Metabolisable Energy, MJ/d or MJ/kgDM of a feed or diet, see also M/D for a diet |
| MER | Metabolisable Energy requirement, MJ/d |
| n | Lactation week number |
| [NCD] | Neutral detergent cellulase [DOMD] in a feed, g/kgDM |
| [ODM] | Oven Dry Matter content of the fresh diet or diet, g/kg |
| [OMD] | Organic Matter Digestibility, g/kg of a diet or feed |

[P], P%          Crude Protein content of milk, g/kg or % per litre
$q_m$             Metabolisability of [GE] at maintenance, [ME]/[GE]
R                Energy retention ($E_f$), MJ/d, scaled by fasting metabolism (F)
TDMI             Total Dry Matter Intake of a diet, kg/head/d
W                Liveweight of the animal, kg
$\Delta$W or LWG  Liveweight gain or change, $\pm$ g or kg/d
$W_c$             Calf birthweight, kg
$W_m$             Mature bodyweight of the dam, kg
$W_n$             Liveweight of the animal in week n of lactation, kg
$W_o$             Total weight of lambs at birth, kg
Y                Yield of milk, kg/d

## 4.11 REFERENCES

AGRICULTURAL AND FOOD RESEARCH COUNCIL (AFRC), (1990) AFRC Technical Committee on Responses to Nutrients, Report No. 5, Nutritive Requirements of Ruminant Animals: Energy. *Nutrition Abstracts and Reviews (Series B)* **60**, 731-804.

AGRICULTURAL AND FOOD RESEARCH COUNCIL (AFRC), (1993) Energy and Protein Requirements of Ruminants. *An advisory manual prepared by the AFRC Technical Committee on Responses to Nutrients.* CAB International, Wallingford, UK. pp 159.

AGRICULTURAL RESEARCH COUNCIL (ARC), (1965) Nutrient Requirements of Farm Livestock No. 2. ARC, London, pp 264.

AGRICULTURAL RESEARCH COUNCIL (ARC), (1980) The Nutrient requirements of Ruminant Livestock. Commonwealth Agricultural Bureaux, Farnham Royal, pp 351.

BECKER R. B., DIX ARNOLD P.T. and MARSHALL S P (1950) Changes in the weight of reproductive organs of the dairy cow and their relation to long-term feeding investigations. *Journal of Dairy Science,* **33**, 911-917.

BICKEL H. and LANDIS J. (1978) Feed evaluation for ruminants. 3. Proposed application of the new system of energy evaluation in Switzerland. *Livestock Production Science,* **5**, 367-372.

BRETT D. J., CORBETT J. L. and INSKIP M. W. (1972) Estimation of the energy value of ewes milk. *Proceedings of the Australian Society of Animal Production,* **9**, 286-291.

BRONSCH K., FREESE H. H., HAGEMEISTER H., KAUFMANN W., KIRCHGESSNER M., MENKE K H., OSLAGE H. J., ROHR K. and VOGT H. (1979) Nettoenergie-Laktation (NEL) - die neue energetische Futterbewertung für Milchkühe. *Deutsche Landwirtschafts-Gesellschaft-Mitteilungen,* Heft 11, **7**, 672.

COATES D.B. and PENNING P.D. (2000) Measuring Animal Performance. In: 't Mannetje L. and Jones R.M. (eds.) *Field and Laboratory Methods for Grassland and Animal Production Research.* CABI Publishing Wallingford, UK. pp. 353-402.

CORBETT J. L. (1978) Measuring sward performance. In: L't Mannetje (ed). *Measurement of Grassland Vegetation and Production,* Commonwealth Agricultural Bureaux, Farnham Royal, pp 163-231.

CORBETT J. L. (1990) Feeding standards for Australian livestock. *Standing Committee on Agriculture, Ruminants Subcommittee,* CSIRO Australia.

FOX D. G., SNIFFEN C. J., O'CONNOR J. D., RUSSELL J. B. and VAN SOEST P. J. (1992) A net carbohydrate and protein system for evaluating cattle diets: 111. Cattle requirements and diet adequacy. *Journal of Animal Science,* **70**, 3578-3596.

DONEY J. M., PEART J. N., SMITH W. F. and LAUDA F. (1979) A consideration of the techniques for estimation of milk yield by suckled sheep and a comparison of estimates obtained by two methods in relation to effect of breed, level of production and stage of lactation. *Journal of Agricultural Science, Cambridge*, **92**, 123-132.

DOWMAN M. G. and COLLINS F. C. (1982) The use of enzymes to predict digestibility of animal feeds. *Journal of Science, Food and Agriculture*, **33**, 689.

GIVENS D. I., EVERINGTON J. M. and ADAMSON A. H. (1990) The nutritive value of spring grass herbage produced on farms throughout England and Wales over 4 years. III. The prediction of energy value from various laboratory measurements. *Animal Feed Science*, **27**, 185-196.

HARKINS J., EDWARDS R. A. and McDONALD P. (1974) A new net energy system for ruminants. *Animal Production,* 19, 141-148.

INRA (1978) Alimentation des Ruminants. Ed INRA Publications, 78000 Versailles.

JAGUSCH K. T. (1968) The utilisation of energy by milk-fed lambs with special reference to the composition of the gain. *PhD Thesis, University of Sydney.*

LANGLANDS J. P. and SUTHERLAND H. A. M. (1968) An estimate of the nutrients utilised for pregnancy by Merino sheep. *British Journal of Nutrition*, **22**, 217-227.

LE DU Y. L. P., BAKER R. D. and BARKER J. M. (1978) The use of short term secretion rate measurements for estimating the milk production of suckler cows. *Journal of Dairy Research*, **45**, 1-4.

LE DU Y. L. P., MACDONALD A.J. and PEART J. N. (1979) Comparison of two techniques for estimating the milk production of suckler cows. *Livestock Production Science*, **6**, 277-281.

LOGAN V. S. and PIGDEN W. D. (1969) Estimating herbage yield from energy intake of grazing ruminants. Experimental Methods for Evaluating Herbage. *Publication 1315, Canadian Department of Agriculture*, pp. 223.

MacHARDY V.F. (1966) Simplified ration formulation. *9th International Congress of Animal Production, Edinburgh* p25, Oliver and Boyd, Edinburgh. pp.25

MINISTRY OF AGRICULTURE, FISHERIES AND FOOD (MAFF), (1975) Energy allowances and feeding systems for ruminants. *Technical bulletin 33*, London, HMSO.

NATIONAL RESEARCH COUNCIL (NRC), (1978). "Nutrient Requirements of Sheep" 5th Revised Edition, National Academy Press, Washington, DC.

NATIONAL RESEARCH COUNCIL (NRC), (1982) United States-Canadian Tables of Feed Composition. National Academy Press, Washington, DC.

NATIONAL RESEARCH COUNCIL (NRC), (1984). "Nutrient Requirements of Beef Cattle" 6th Revised Edition, National Academy Press, Washington, DC.

NATIONAL RESEARCH COUNCIL (NRC), (1989). "Nutrient requirements of Dairy Cattle" 6th Revised Edition, National Academy Press, Washington, DC.

RUSSELL J. B., O'CONNOR J. D., FOX D. G., VAN SOEST P. J. and SNIFFEN C. J. (1992) A net carbohydrate and protein system for evaluating cattle diets: 1. Carbohydrate and protein availability. *Journal of Animal Science,* **70**, 3551-3561.

SCHIEMANN R., NEHRING K., HOFFMANN L., JENTSCH W. and CHUDY, A (1971) Energetische Futterbewertung und Energienormen. VEB *Deutscher Landwirstschafts Verlag*, Berlin, 344pp.

SNIFFEN C. J., O'CONNOR J. D., VAN SOEST P. J., FOX D. G. and RUSSELL J. B. (1992) A net carbohydrate and protein system for evaluating cattle diets: 11. Carbohydrate and protein availability. *Journal of Animal Science*, 70, 3562-3577.

SOMERVILLE S. J. and LOWMAN B. G. (1980) A Comparison of machine-milking and the calf-suckling technique as methods of measuring the milk yield of beef cows. *Animal Production*, **30**,365-372.

TERRY R. A., OSBOURN D. F., CAMMELL S. B. and FENLON J. S. (1973) *In vitro* digestibility and the estimation of energy in herbage. *Proceedings of the 5th General Meeting, European Grassland Federation*, Uppsala, Sweden, Vaxtodling **28**, pp. 19-25.

TILLEY M. A. and TERRY R. A. (1963) A two-stage technique for the *in vitro* digestion of forage crops. *Journal of the British Grassland Society*, **18**, 104-111.

TISSIER M., THERIEZ M., GUEGUEN L. and MOLENAT G. (1978). Ovine, In: INRA (ed.). *Alimentation des Ruminants*. INRA Publications, Versailles, pp 597.

TYRELL H. F. and REID J. T. (1965) Prediction of energy value of cows milk. *Journal of Dairy Science*, **48**, 1215-1223.

VAN ES A. J. H. (1978) Feed evaluation for ruminants. 1. The system in use from May 1977 in the Netherlands. *Livestock Production Science*, **5**, 331-345.

VERMOREL M. (1978) Feed evaluation for ruminants. 2. The new energy system proposed in France. *Livestock Production Science*, **5**, 347-365.

VERMORAL M., COULON J. B. and JOURNET M. (1987) Revision du systeme des unites fourrages (UF). *Bulletin Technical C.R.Z.V. Theix, I.N.R.A.* **70**, 9-18.

# CHAPTER 5

# MEASUREMENT OF HERBAGE INTAKE AND INGESTIVE BEHAVIOUR BY HOUSED ANIMALS

**R. Baumont, M. Chenost and C. Demarquilly**

## 5.1 INTRODUCTION

Measurement of the amount of fresh herbage eaten by housed (zero grazed) animals may have various objectives:

i.     To study the effect of "physiological" changes with age of plants during successive growth cycles, and of environmental factors on the intake of the main herbage species. This type of study is usually carried out in conjunction with a measure of digestibility.

ii.     To study intake changes following various methods of conservation by measuring the amount of herbage/forage consumed before and after conservation.

iii.     To study intake differences between plants of different varieties or species particularly for plant breeding purposes.

iv.     To estimate the amount of herbage consumed by the productive animal zero grazed in the summer, to specify the quantity and quality of supplement required to meet production targets.

v.     To estimate the herbage intake of the grazing animal and the factors influencing that intake. It is simpler and more precise to measure this for housed animals than for those grazing at pasture.

Intake measurements are often made together with measurements of ingestive behaviour (see review by Burns *et al.*, 1994). Over the last decade many experimental efforts were aimed at developing recording techniques to study ingestive behaviour at pasture as well as indoor. Analysis of ingestive behaviour is helpful for a better understanding of variations in intake.

In this chapter the experimental constraints and the value of measurements of intake made indoors, compared with those of animals grazing similar herbage in the field, are discussed. Ingestive behaviour measurement techniques are discussed in order to assess in what terms indoor behavioural parameters are useful to understand behaviour at pasture. For specific technical aspects (materials, equipment, experimental procedures) see publications by the following authors (Minson *et al.*, 1976; Heaney *et al.*, 1968; Cammell, 1977; Zemelink, 1980; Burns *et al.*, 1994).

## 5.2. MEASUREMENT OF THE AMOUNT CONSUMED

Whatever the objective in measuring herbage intake it is important to know to what extent conditions of harvesting or conditioning, and methods of feeding affect the amount consumed indoors and whether the results can be extrapolated to other animals.

### 5.2.1 Harvesting and conditioning of herbage

The following factors can influence the amount of harvested herbage consumed:
- type of presentation (long, lacerated or chopped);
- height of cut;
- previous management of the pasture (cut or grazed);
- frequency of cutting, duration and method of storage of grass between harvesting and feeding.

5.2.1.1 *Harvesting machinery*. Herbage cut with a finger bar mower and harvested in the long form, can be picked up either manually with a fork or mechanically by the pick-up of a self-loading trailer. More commonly, herbage is harvested with the following types of forage harvester:
- flail type, which lacerates and breaks down the forage into lengths of 10-20 cm;
- double chop, which gives a shorter chop of 5-15 cm;
- precision chop, which produces forage of 0.5-5 cm lengths depending on the setting of the machine.

Chopped versus long herbage

In an experiment with sheep, Dulphy (unpublished) offered first growth tall fescue either un-chopped (cut with a mower and picked up with a fork) or chopped (2-4 cm long using a chaff cutter). The dry matter intake by two groups of six sheep are shown in Table 5.1. Chopping slightly increased the amount eaten, the animals spent slightly longer feeding on the chopped forage (15-20 min d-1) and had a greater rate of intake.

Chopped versus lacerated herbage

Tayler and Rudman (1965) studied the amount consumed and the performance of steers on the same forages either harvested with a flail type harvester or cut with a finger bar mower and picked up with a chopper type forage harvester. The animals fed

*Table 5.1. Effect of chopping on the amount of first growth tall fescue eaten by sheep (Dulphy, unpublished).*

|  | DM intake g/kg $W^{0.75}$ | |
|---|---|---|
|  | Long | Chopped |
| Pre-heading | 57.7 (100) | 61.4 (106) |
| Heading | 50.3 (100) | 54.6 (109) |

on chopped grass consumed slightly more dry matter than those fed on lacerated grass (Table 5.2). The authors showed that the differences were more important with mature forage because the flail type harvester mixed the dead parts of the plant with the green parts making selection by the animal more difficult.

The same authors found that the effect of laceration was event more marked when the forage was harvested from a sward previously grazed (Table 5.3). On average the liveweight grains of the steers were from 3 to 25 % lower with the lacerated grass than with the grass mown and then chopped. This decrease in the intake of lacerated forage,

*Table 5.2. Effect of method of harvesting on the herbage consumption of steers (Tayler and Rudman, 1965).*

|  | DM Intake (kg $day^{-1}$) | |
|---|---|---|
|  | Flail forage harvester | Mower and chopper blower |
| Forage harvested |  |  |
| in spring | 4.81 (100) | 4.94 (103) |
| in summer | 5.58 (100) | 5.95 (107) |

*Table 5.3. Effects of method of harvesting and previous grazing on herbage consumption by steers (Tayler and Rudman, 1965).*

|  | DM Intake (kg $day^{-1}$) | |
|---|---|---|
|  | Flail forage harvester | Mower and chopper blower |
| Sward previously cut | 6.26 (100) | 6.38 (102) |
| Sward previously grazed | 3.59 (100) | 4.76 (133) |

which can have a marked effect on the performance of the animals, was also found by Michalet-Doreau and Dulphy (unpublished) with dry ewes fed on a 3rd cut of Italian ryegrass either lacerated (flail type harvester) or chopped (precision chop harvester), the decrease being 13 %.

Indirect evidence of the influence of type of forage harvester on herbage intake was also found by Demarquilly (1970) when studying the artificial drying of forage. The intake of dehydrated grasses harvested with a flail type harvester was lower (15.4 %) than the intake of corresponding green forage (cut with a motor mower and then chopped into lengths of 2-4 cm with a chaff cutter). In contrast the intake of dehydrated grasses harvested with a double chop or precision chop harvester was slightly higher (3.4 %) than the intake of the corresponding green forages.

It can be concluded from these studies that the form of presentation (long, chopped or lacerated) affects the amount of fresh herbage consumed by ruminants, and consequently affects their performance. The presentation which gives the greatest intake seems to be herbage, chopped into lengths of 2-4 cm. It is well known that reducing the size of forage particles increases intake by an increase of intake rate (Jarrige et al., 1973; Jarrige et al., 1995) and that animals prefer the feeds they can eat faster (Kenney and Black, 1984). Chopping limits selection by the animals, in particular by sheep and goats indoors, so that the composition and digestibility of the herbage consumed are very similar to that offered, at least when the proportion of refusals allowed is limited (c 10 %). When studying the influence of conservation on intake of forages, it is preferable that the green forage fed indoors and the conserved forage, are harvested with the same machine and cut at the same height.

5.2.1.2 *Cutting height*. Harvesters normally cut the grass at a height of 5-7 cm above ground level, but the cutting height can vary considerably depending on the setting of the machine. There is only limited evidence available, however, on the influence of height of cutting on amount of grass consumed.

Tayler and Rudman (1965) compared the growth rates of steers offered grass cut at 6.5 to 10 cm above ground level, either with a finger bar mower and then picked up with a chopper type harvester, or with a flail type harvester (Table 5.4). The lower cut (at 6.5 cm) gave slightly lower animal performance. Differences in performance were more marked (Table 5.5) when the animals were offered either the top fraction of the sward (cut at 13.5 cm above ground level), or the bottom fraction (the remainder cut at 6.5 cm). As the digestibility measured *in vitro*, was practically the same for top and

Table 5.4. *Effect of method of harvesting fresh herbage on the liveweight gain (kg day⁻¹) of steers (Tayler and Rudman, 1965).*

|  | Flail forage harvester | Mower and chopper blower |
|---|---|---|
| Cut at 10 cm above ground | 0.84 | 0.91 |
| Cut at 6.5 cm above ground | 0.71 | 0.81 |

*Table 5.5. Effect of fraction of sward on liveweight gain (kg day$^{-1}$) of steers (Taylor and Rudman, 1965).*

|         | Top fraction | Bottom fraction |
|---------|--------------|-----------------|
| Spring  | 0.89         | 0.58            |
| Summer  | 0.74         | 0.64            |

bottom fractions of herbage in these experiments, the observed intake differences must have been attributable to the amounts consumed. The authors explained the reduced intakes by differences in the morphological characteristics of the forage (smaller proportion of leaves), the greater proportion of weeds and debris and a higher level of rust infection in the bottom fraction. In many cases, contamination of forage by soil would also occur, particularly when a cut is taken close to ground level.

Although the effect of height of cutting on amounts consumed has not been fully quantified, it is important that the cut should be taken at he same height when comparing intakes of a conserved forage to that of standing green forage. The cut should also be taken at the height of the stubble left after grazing by cattle, when the intake of grazed grass is to be estimated.

5.2.1.3 *Influence of previous grazing.* Intake of grass can be affected by its contamination with animal excreta from the previous grazing of the pasture. Animals in pens cannot eat as selectively as grazing animals and this significantly lowers their intake compared with grazing animals. This has been noted by several authors (Hutton, 1962; Demarquilly, 1966; Chenost and Demarquilly, 1969; Tayler and Rudman, 1965). Tayler and Rudman (Table 5.3) observed a significant decrease in the amounts of grass consumed when it was harvested from a field previously grazed compared with a field previously cut; the decrease being 25 % for grass harvested by finger bar mower and 43 % for grass harvested by flail type harvester. In a trial with dairy cows (Demarquilly, 1966), the decrease was on average 42 % when the grass was cut with a finger bar mower and manually harvested with a fork. Therefore it would appear that estimates of the intake of a crop harvested from a previously grazed field may give a considerable underestimation of the intake of this herbage grazed *in situ*.

5.2.1.4 *Effect of cutting frequency.* Studies carried out at the Grassland Research Institute, Hurley, show that herbage cut once daily can satisfactorily be fed in one or two feeds per day (Grassland Research Institute, 1966). Studies in Ireland (Collins, 1973) have shown a significant decrease in the amount of herbage consumed if harvesting is carried out less frequently. Decreases in the amounts of dry matter consumed compared with immediate feeding varied between 6-7 %, 19-20 % and 25-26 % depending on whether the grass was cut at 24, 48 or 72 hours before feeding, respectively. This author does not however specify the type of presentation nor the method of storage of the grass (in a trailer or in heaps of different sizes).

In numerous measurements of the amounts of grass consumed indoors carried out at I.N.R.A., (1500 measurements of one week on sheep and 300 on cattle) grass was cut every morning except at weekends, and during these days a lower intake was never noted. However, the grass for sheep cut on Friday and fed on Saturday and Sunday was stored after chopping, in a cold room at + 4°C, and the grass cut for cattle on Saturday and fed long on Sunday was stored under cover in a thin layer (20 cm). It is important that the herbage does not heat during storage and that the dry matter content does not increase, as the wilting of a herbage with a low dry matter content tends to increase the amount consumed (Demarquilly, 1966; Grassland Research Institute, 1966); The recommended cutting frequency by most authors varies from once to twice daily (Meijs, 1979).

The reason for the recommendations of two cuts a day is in order to feed the herbage as fresh as possible and to avoid the heating which takes place during storage and in the trough. This is particularly noticeable if it is left in a heap and particularly when it has been lacerated. When herbage is cut once a day, and even more so when it is cut for feeding over a period of two days (e.g. Saturday and Sunday), it is important to use a cold store, or to store it under cover in a thin layer, particularly in hot and humid conditions.

5.2.1.5 *Long-term storage*. Daily cutting and feeding of herbage can under certain circumstances present some difficulties which make it necessary for a whole field to be harvested and stored, for example:
- in wet areas where it is not possible to use harvesting machinery every day;
- in comparing intakes of plants before and after conservation, which necessitates cutting on the same day;
- in measuring the intake of forages harvested at different times of the year which have to be made simultaneously to eliminate the seasonal effects on the voluntary intake by the animal;
- when rapid changes in vegetative stages of some herbages take place during intake measurements.

Only methods of storage which do not, or only slightly affect intake and nutritive value of grass can be used, namely drying and freezing.

Minson (1966) and Minson *et al.* (1976) in Australia, showed that drying at 100°C for 6 hours followed by cooling for 8 hours did not affect the voluntary intake of tropical grasses by comparison with green forage. Temperatures above 100°C which can lead to a darkening of the material are not advisable. Simple driers adapted to the requirements of measuring feeding value (digestibility and intake) of fodder crops have been successfully devised in Australia. These enable drying of 0.5 tonnes of forage daily. To avoid losses and to facilitate sampling, the dried grass is coarsely chopped (2-5 cm) and blown into bags containing 4 kg of dry forage which facilitate subsequent feeding.

Demarquilly (1970) did not observe differences in digestibility or intake between fresh grass and grass artificially dehydrated at low temperature when fed in the chopped form to sheep, but for red clover he observed a decrease of 10 % in the amount consumed and 6 percentage units in digestibility. Using the same type of machine, Vérité and Journet (1970) found with dairy cows, that drying led to a limited but significant increase in the amounts of dry matter consumed by comparison with fresh grass (13.62 against 13.07 kg) but this increase varied from day to day (- 1.72 to + 3.82 kg with an average of + 0.55 kg). The difference appeared to be partly due to the presence of external moisture on the fresh plant since the increase in intake due to drying was 0.86 kg for wet grass (n = 18) and only 0.36 kg (n = 24) for grass with no surface moisture. The increase was also due to the dry matter content of fresh grass since drying only increases the amount consumed when fresh grass had a dry matter content of less than 18 %. In only 2 out of 23 comparisons made by Heaney et al. (1966) did drying significantly affect (one increase, one decrease) the amount of green grass lucerne mixtures consumed.

Thus it can be concluded that although drying does not on average affect the intake of grass, it can however increase it slightly in the case of very wet grasses (< 18 % DM), and sometimes decrease it in the case of legumes with a high water content which are difficult to dry. However, drying can lead to a decrease in the digestibility of organic matter and of protein. It is therefore advisable to dry at a temperature between 80 and 100°C up to a dry matter content of 87-88 % as recommended by Minson et al. (1976).

Freezing, when carried out rapidly, can also be used for storage of herbage and is unlikely to greatly affect the intake of herbage (Pigden et al., 1961). Heaney et al. (1966) observed however a low intake of legumes after freezing, which they attributed to the high water content of the samples studied, which led to physical disruption of the cells during freezing.

Further studies are therefore necessary to establish under which conditions freezing can affect (increase or decrease) intake of green forage. The results so far however tend to confirm those of Raymond et al. (1953) and Van Es and Van der Honing (1976) with grasses, that freezing does not, or only slightly modifies the digestibility of organic matter and nitrogen of herbage. However, MacRae et al. (1975) observed in nitrogen balance trials that freezing led to an important decrease in nitrogen solubility.

## 5.2.2 Feeding methods

When it is necessary to know the voluntary intake of herbage it is important to make sure that the animal can effectively consume the maximum amount of herbage. Also it is important to make the most effective use of the facilities. In planning a trial the following should therefore be given consideration:
- How much herbage to offer?
- How many feeds per day and what duration of access to the feed?
- How long should preliminary and experimental periods be?
- How many animals are needed?

5.2.2.1 *Amount of herbage offered.* The term "voluntary intake" assumes that the intake by the animal is not limited by the amount offered. It is thus necessary that the amount of herbage offered should be greater than the amount the animal is able to consume.

Tayler and Rudman (1965) showed with growing cattle kept indoors that their intake increased with the quantity offered until refusals of 25-30 % occurred. Although it would seem advisable to aim for this level of refusal to ensure that the amounts consumed are near maximum, large refusals enable the animal to eat with greater selectivity. The composition and characteristics of the herbage eaten may therefore be different from that offered. This problem, which applies particularly to pastures with mixed species, is of lesser importance with young grass but becomes more relevant as the grass matures (Greenhalgh and Runcie, 1962) and for tropical forages (Zemmelink, 1980). A reasonable compromise is achieved by feeding herbage in such amounts that refusals are not higher than 10-15 % of the offered quantities (Cammell, 1977). In our studies we have opted for a 10 % refusal level, but all the green forages are chopped beforehand to reduce the possibilities of selection by the animal.

5.2.2.2 *Number of feeds and time of access to feed.* As shown above, fresh herbage can satisfactorily be harvested once a day and sometimes only every two days, in order to reduce weekend work. The number of feeds offered per day is another important consideration affecting the workload. Campbell and Merilan (1961) compared the daily amounts of dry matter consumed by dairy cows fed 2, 4 or 7 times a day with lucerne hay and concentrate feeds. The highest dry matter intake of 19.1 kg was obtained with 4 feeds per day compared with 17.7 kg for 2 feeds. Increasing the number of feeds to 7 did not further increase the level of intake. However, the time of access to feed was limited to 3 hours after each feed, thus for 2 feeds, only 6 hours feeding time was available, which is inadequate to allow maximum intake, particularly for a diet rich in concentrates (60 %). Three feeding frequencies of late-cut grass hay (two times per day at 8h interval, two times per day at 12 h interval, once a day) were compared with continuous access to the feed (Dulphy *et al.*, 1988). The daily voluntary intake was not significantly affected by the number of feedings nor by the interval between feeds although it tended to be lower with only one feeding per day.

Blaxter *et al.* (1961) showed that when access to feed was limited to a minimum of 18 hours, the amount consumed by sheep fed 4 times at 6 hour intervals was not significantly different from the amount consumed by sheep receiving 2 equal feeds at 12 hour intervals. Similarly, Dulphy and Demarquilly (unpublished) did not observe any decrease in intake when the number of feeds per day was reduced from 3 to 2. To measure the amount of fresh herbage consumed indoors, it is therefore feasible to use a system of 2 feeds per day, with the collection and weighing of refusals every morning, before the first feed of the day. However, care must be taken where small mangers are used. The squeezing of herbage into small mangers, particularly if the herbage was harvested by a flail mower, can lead to heating in the base of the feed, and to reduced intake.

The amount of herbage consumed depends much more on the time of access to feed than on the number of feeds. Demarquilly and Dulphy (1977) have shown that with two feeds of fresh grass per day, the intake during the two main feeding periods (each lasting 80 minutes) which follow the two feeds represents only 45-50 % and 55-65 % respectively, for heifers and for sheep of their total daily intake. The remainder of the intake is made up with more numerous (2 to 10 depending upon herbage quality) and shorter (20 to 35 minutes) feeds spread throughout the day. The effects on intake of limiting time of access to forage (twice 1h30 vs. continuous access) are dependent on the forage quality (Baumont et al., 1988). Voluntary intake was maintained with limited time of access for a low quality grass hay, but not for a high quality lucerne hay.

5.2.2.3 *Preliminary and experimental periods*. There is little experimental information available for ruminants on the number of days taken to reach maximum intake levels. It is important that these levels are reached before the measurement period commences.

Blaxter et al. (1961) showed that sheep fed on poor quality hay reached their maximum level of intake after 9-12 days. The same authors point out that in some experiments it can take as long as 15 days, and that daily fluctuations of intake make the definition of the timing of maximum intake difficult.

Preliminary periods of feeding normally vary from 10-14 days. The period can be reduced to 7 days for herbage studies (Demarquilly and Weiss, 1970) when the animals are already well adapted to the grass. During this period the objective of the experimenter will be to achieve the maximum level of intake as quickly as possible, feeding to a refusal of 10-15 % in spite of variations in intake from day to day.

Various methods of feeding are used:
- Sequential feeding methods which consist of feeding an amount of forage equal to 1.15 times that consumed the previous two days. The drawback to this method is that it increases the duration of the preliminary period. In the case of sudden and sporadic drops of intake (e.g. 30 % below the intake level of the proceeding day) the amount of feed calculated for the following day is likely to be too low. For this reason Blaxter et al. (1961) suggest a modified sequential feeding system which consists of adjusting the amount of feed for the following day, only when refusals are below 15 % of the amount offered.
- The method used at the Grassland Research Institute, Hurley (Cammell, 1977) consists of adjusting the level of feeding for a given day to 1.15 times that of 2 days before.

The experimenter must use his/her own experience to minimise the effect of daily variations in amounts consumed by changes in the amounts offered. In our studies on sheep, we aim at an average refusal of 10 % (but the forages offered are chopped, which limits the possibility of selection) with daily variations between 5 and 15 %.

The length of the measurement period after establishing maximum consumption is often 10-15 days, a period which results in errors of measurement of about ± 2 % (Blaxter et al., 1961). However, the results may not be of great value if during these periods significant changes occur in chemical composition, stage of growth and digestibility of herbage. Therefore in our series of experiments designed to study "physiological" changes with age of plant, we have opted for periods of 6 days, with an interval of one day between periods. On the day between periods when the amount consumed is not measured, it is essential that the animals are fed *ad libitum*.

5.2.2.4 *Number of animals*. It is well established that the amount of feed consumed depends on the season, the ambient temperature, and the size, breed and physiological conditions of the animals. It is thus important to standardise these parameters if the amount consumed has to reflect accurately the typical intake characteristics of the forage. In most experiments, environmental conditions are standardised across treatments and the main source of variation remaining is the variation between individual animals.

The variations in intake between animals is important in deciding how many animals are required per treatment. For sheep the coefficient of variation for intake of conserved forages varies between 10 and 15 %, excluding results for straw and silage (Crampton *et al.*, 1960; Blaxter *et al.*, 1961; Heaney *et al.*, 1968). It seems, however, that the variability is slightly less for fresh forages. Michalet-Doreau and Demarquilly (unpublished) have calculated the variability of the measurements of the amounts consumed using 26 different lots of 6 sheep, each of which had received 50 samples of fresh forage chosen at random among 1200 samples studied in their laboratory. The standard deviation (SD) was 6.9 g/kg W0.75 and the coefficient of variation (CV) 9 %. This variability is smaller than that (10.5 %) calculated by Minson *et al.* (1964). The variation can be decreased (SD = 4.9; CV = 7 %) if the values which differ from the mean by more than two standard deviations are ignored. Using this premise it was possible to draw two curves (Figure 5.1) which give the number of animals necessary to detect a given difference in the amounts consumed. With 6 sheep per group it is possible to detect differences of 11 g/kg $W^{0.75}$ (curve 1) and of 8 g/kg $W^{0.75}$ (curve 2) in intake at the 5 % significance level.

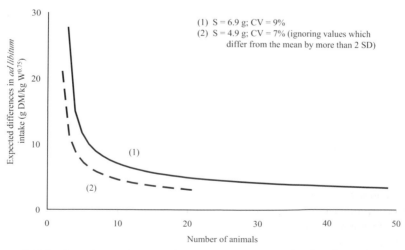

*Figure 5.1 Number of animals required to give an 80% probability that the intake difference will be significant at the 5% level (Michalet-Doreau and Demarquilly, unpublished).*

Some workers (e.g. Minson *et al.*, 1976) have used 8-10 sheep per trial, but because of the complexity involved, most authors work with 6 animals per trial. This number has been adopted by Demarquilly and Weiss (1970) to establish the French tables of feeding values for forage. This number was also recommended by Heaney (1979).

5.2.3 The value and use of measurements of herbage intake

When a measure of the amount consumed is obtained for a given forage, the value may be used for the following:
- to describe the true intake characteristics of forage;
- to extrapolate this value to other types of animals or other species.

As discussed earlier, the amount of a forage voluntarily consumed by a ruminant depends not only on its intake characteristics of this forage (called "ingestibility") but also on the intake capacity (often wrongly called appetite) of the animal on which the measurement is made. This intake capacity depends on the following:
- weight, age, physiological state (growth, lactation, fattening) and feeding history of the animal, as well as species and breed;
- environmental conditions (climate, season, indoor conditions) in which the measurements are made.

The sources of variation related to environmental conditions can be easily eliminated if care is taken to make the measurements at the same period of time and under the same environmental conditions, as for example when comparing the intake of species or varieties of plants grown around the same time. However, when differences are found in the intake of herbages grown at different times of the year, these could be attributed to differences in herbage characteristics, to different animal characteristics, or to different environmental conditions. There is strong evidence that the annual variations in voluntary intake of Texel wethers are mainly related to seasonal changes in food intake in relation to the length of day (Michalet-Doreau and Gatel, 1983; Thompson *et al.*, 1985), Voluntary intake of hay is the lowest in February and the highest in August with a mean amplitude of 25% (Michalet-Doreau and Gatel, 1988). However not all the sheep breeds are sensitive to the length of day and cattle are less sensitive than sheep. Seasonal effect on voluntary intake can only be taken into account by making measurements at the same time, of the intake of corresponding dried or frozen herbage or by comparison with the intake of a standard forage (for example a standard hay) as proposed by Evans and Potter (1984) and Abrams *et al.*, (1987).

Other sources of variation related to the animal (except for live weight), are more difficult to eliminate. The effect of live weight can be easily accounted for by expressing the amount consumed per kg of metabolic weight ($W^{0.75}$). This notation has been adopted by most of the authors interested in intake of feeds since it was recommended at the 3rd Symposium of Energy Metabolism (Kleiber, 1965). With sheep fed fresh ryegrass, it was shown that voluntary intake or voluntary intake per 100 kg live weight are significantly correlated with animal's liveweight. On the contrary, voluntary intake per kg $W^{0.75}$ is independent of live weight (Demarquilly and Andrieu, 1987). When comparing different animal species varying in body size metabolic weight is not the best way to correct voluntary intake data, as forage intake depends not only on energy needs but also on the development of the digestive tract which varies markedly with the live weight (Dulphy et al., 1994). Expressing the data per kg $W^{0.9}$ was found to eliminate the effect of live weight on intake when comparing sheep and cattle data (Baumont, 1989).

Other factors can also affect the voluntary intake of the animal, namely age and physiological state, stage of lactation and level of milk production, stage of fattening and feeding history, and also breed. This implies that measurements of amounts consumed indoors should be made on:

- Animals as similar as possible from one experiment to another if the main interest is variations in herbage intake in relation to age, growth stage, number of cuts and type of herbage. In the case of long term experiments, "standard" animals will have to be changed periodically.

The majority of researchers interested in the intake of forage plants have for reasons of ease and cost, measured intakes on castrated male sheep. These intakes expressed in g/kg $W^{0.75}$ are not directly applicable to cattle and lactating ewes. However, the ranking of the intakes observed with castrated male sheep tend to remain the same for other categories of ruminants (Blaxter and Wilson, 1962; Blaxter et al., 1966; Buchman and Henken, 1964; Ingalls et al., 1965; Demarquilly and Weiss, 1971). Intakes measured on sheep can also be quantitatively related to the amounts consumed by cattle. Intake measurements made simultaneously on "standard" sheep (castrated Texel rams, 1.5-3 years old and weighing on average 60 kg) and cattle at CRZV at Theix showed a close relationship between intake of forage by cattle (y) and intake by sheep (x), the two values being expressed in g DM/kg $W^{0.75}$ (Figure 5.2). These relationship can be expressed by the following two equations:

Dairy cows of 600 kg producing 25 kg of milk

$$y = 78.0 + 0.826 \, x \quad (\pm 7.4; \, n = 74; \, r = 0.82) \tag{5.1}$$

Dairy Friesian heifers of 400 kg

$$y = 22.4 + 0.969 \, x \quad (\pm 4.8; \, n = 31; \, r = 0.87) \tag{5.2}$$

These equations have been used to establish the fill unit (FU) system (INRA (1979); Jarrige et al., 1979; 1986; Dulphy et al., 1989; Jarrige et al., 1986). The reference forage that contains one FU per kg DM is an average pasture grass cut at the grazing stage of the first growth. The voluntary dry matter intake (VDMI) of this reference forage amounts to 75 g DM/kg $W^{0.75}$ in the standard sheep, to 95 g DM/kg $W^{0.75}$ in the standard cattle, a Friesian heifer, and to 140 g DM/kg $W^{0.75}$ in the standard lactating cow. Each forage has been given three fill values per kg DM expressed in FU for sheep, cattle and lactating cow respectively. For a given forage the three FU are

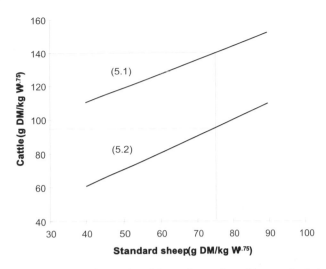

*Figure 5.2 Relationship between the intake of forage by cattle and by standard sheep (Dulphy et al., 1989).*

calculated by the ratio between the VDMI of the reference forage and the VDMI of the forage in question. Thus, sheep FU equals 75/VDMI by sheep, cattle FU equals 95/VDMI by cattle and lactating FU equals 140/VDMI by cow. Each category of animal defined by its live weight, physiological stage, level of milk production, and, sometimes breed, has a feed intake capacity expressed by one value in FU. The system enables the voluntary intake of various categories of ruminants to be expressed in FU, and the intake of the various forages also expressed in FU, to be estimated, whether these forages are fed alone or together with concentrate feeds.

## 5.3 RECENT ADVANCES IN INTAKE AND INGESTIVE BEHAVIOUR MEASUREMENTS INDOORS

Many experimental efforts have been developed since the 50's to analyse ingestive behaviour of stall feed animals (Balch, 1958) and its relationship with the variations of voluntary intake (Dulphy *et al.*, 1980). Ingestive behaviour can be studied by visual observation. But the most widespread method has been to assess ingestive behaviour by recording the jaw movements using a small balloon fitted in the submandibular space and connected to a pressure recorder (Ruckebusch, 1963). Over the last 15 years the tremendous advances in electronic and computer sciences has allowed many improvements in the recording of intake and ingestive behaviour indoors.

### 5.3.1 Eating time

Variations in eating time between forages are not related to voluntary intake and thus eating time is not useful to predict intake. However, measuring eating time together with intake is helpful to characterise several attributes of the forage like intake, ease of prehension and resistance to mastication.

5.3.1.1 *Recording methods.* Visual observation is certainly the most accurate way to assess eating time but it is very difficult to make recordings for long periods. Recording on videotape provides many data for short term studies but its use over long periods is limited due to subsequent very time consuming analysis of the tapes. Recording of jaw movements on paper charts enables easy distinctions between eating periods and rumination periods. Jaw movements during rumination are remarkably regular in amplitude and frequency whereas, during eating, they are irregular due to small interruptions and alternation between prehension and mastication sequences. But analysis of traces of jaw movements on paper charts is also very tedious and time consuming. Electronic devices (see also Chapter 6) enable automatic recording of jaw movements (Penning, 1983; Brun *et al.*, 1984) and simple computer software have been developed to interpret the events and to assist in data reduction (Brun *et al.*, 1984; Penning *et al.*, 1984; Luginbuhl *et al.*, 1987; Beauchemin *et al.*, 1989; Baumont *et al.*, 1990, Baumont and Brun, 1992). Detailed analysis of eating activity was achieved by analogue recording of the jaw movements that enabled the distinction between bites and masticatory jaw movements to be made (Penning, 1983). Most of the systems developed (Brun *et al.*, 1984; Luginbuhl *et al.*, 1987) are mainly aimed at counting jaw movements in order to estimate the time devoted to the different activities. In the system used at I.N.R.A (Figure 5.3) jaw movements are categorised minute by minute to distinguish activities of eating, ruminating, and resting. These data can be displayed in tabular or graphic form and summarised by the hour for further analysis. The major negative attribute of all jaw-movement recording techniques is the need to equip the animals with a halter and a sensing device. It is impossible to avoid data losses completely, due to breakage of the equipment or of the halter, especially when working with young animals which are more nervous than adults. Manual analysis of jaw movement recordings on paper charts, as well as computerised recording and analysis, can lead to some overestimation of eating time as it is very difficult to distinguish between a true eating period and other activities such as licking and self grooming. Overestimation of eating time compared to visual observations was reported by Beauchemin and Buchanan-Smith (1989) and by M. van Os and R. Baumont (unpublished). A way to overcome this problem is to record simultaneously the variations in the weight of feed mangers and to associate these with eating jaw movements (Baumont and Brun, 1992, Figure 5.3).

5.3.1.2 *The use of eating time data: comparison between indoor and grazing situations.* During eating, animals successively take into account three attributes of the forage: its sensory characteristics (commonly called palatability), its ease of prehension and its resistance to mastication. Expressing eating time per kg dry matter ingested is a universal method used to characterise these attributes of feeds. Further analysis of ingestive behaviour to explain differences between feeds can be achieved by recording bite size and bite mass (see below).

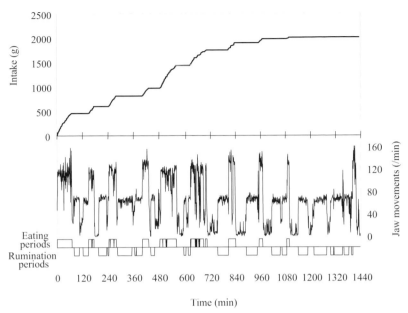

*Figure 5.3 Integrated minute by minute analysis of cumulative daily intake and jaw movement activities in sheep offered lucerne hay ad libitum. Eating periods are defined by a jaw movement rate > 80/min and a simultaneous increase of the cumulative intake curve. Rumination periods are defined by a jaw movement rate between 40 and 80/min without increase in the intake curve. (Baumont and Brun, 1992).*

Factors influencing variation of the time needed to eat one kg forage by stall fed animals were reviewed by Jarrige *et al.* (1995). The amount of crude fibre or of total cell wall in the forage as well as the particle size of the forage are the main factors determining eating time. Thus, eating time increases with the age of the plant during the first and second cycle of growth of green forages. However, large differences exist between grasses and legumes, with legumes at the same vegetative stage as grasses, requiring 30 % less time for ingestion. Effects of chop length of the forage on eating time was clearly established for green and conserved forages. Chop length is particularly important for herbage silages fed to sheep and to a lesser extent when fed to cattle (Dulphy and Demarquilly, 1973)

Only a few comparisons between ingestive behaviour at pasture and indoors have been made. Eating time of animals fed indoors seems to be 30 to 50 % shorter than when grazing (Table 5.6). Animals fed cut herbage indoors have bites which are larger but less frequent than at pasture because animals do not have to search, collect and severe the forage (Jarrige *et al.*, 1995). Indeed, cows eating from a swath of freshly cut lucerne take 5 to 6 times fewer bites per minute, but which are 4 to 7 times larger, than when they graze the same lucerne (Dougherty *et al.*, 1989). Therefore, measurements made indoors are useful to isolate the role of resistance to mastication and eating time from the role of prehension of the herbage which is specific to the grazing situation.

*Table 5.6. Eating (E) and rumination (R) chewing durations of ruminants depending on whether they graze or consume the same grass cut or conserved forages (Jarrige et al., 1995).*

| References | Forages | Animals | Duration (h/day) | | | |
|---|---|---|---|---|---|---|
| | | | Grazing | | Cut forage | |
| | | | E | R | E | R |
| Lofgreen *et al.* (1957) | Lucerne or orchard grass | Cattle | 6.8 | 5.3 | 4.6 | 7.0 |
| | grazed *vs* cut | Sheep | 8.7 | 3.9 | 4.3 | 6.0 |
| Stricklin *et al.* (1976) | Grazed grass *vs* grass silage | Cows | 8.8 | - | 6.1 | - |
| M. Journet *et al.* | Grazed grass *vs* | Dairy | | | | |
| (unpublished) | maize silage (13 kg DM) | Cows | 8.1 | 5.8 | 6.2 | 8.4 |
| Dougherty *et al.* (1989) | Grazed lucerne *vs* | Cows | 74 [jaw movements/min] | | | 83 |
| | freshly cut in a swath | | 26 | [bites/min] | | 5 |

## 5.3.2 Kinetics of intake

Measurement of daily voluntary intake is universal and quantitative analysis of meal patterns can help to understand variations in daily voluntary intake but, recording the duration of the different meals, does not give an estimate of the amounts ingested within meals. Thus, methods were developed to record continuously the evolution of intake during the day in animals fed indoors.

5.3.2.1 *Recording methods.* Continuous recording of the weight of feed boxes can be achieved by suspending them from a balance beam (Suzuki *et al.,* 1969; Metz, 1975; Heinrich and Conrad, 1987) or by placing the feed box on a weight sensor (Putnam *et al.,* 1968; Baile, 1975, Jones and Forbes, 1984; Faverdin, 1985). Weight losses of the mangers were first recorded on paper charts, but digitisation of the output signal, allowed continuous monitoring by microcomputer of the weight of feeders placed on sensors fitted with strain gauges (Baumont *et al.,* 1989; Baumont *et al.,* 1990; Forbes, 1995 and Baumont *et al.,* 1998). Together with monitoring of jaw movements, the system allows a complete analysis of feeding behaviour of stall-fed ruminants (Figure 5.3). The difficulty of this technology is to find the appropriate algorithm in the recording software that damps fluctuations in the weight of the manger during feeding periods that are due to animal activity. The challenge is to record weights of the manger during the small interruptions in feeding that occur in the meal for the animal to masticate and swallow the herbage ingested, because at these times the weight of the feeder is not normally disturbed by animal activity. In the system used at I.N.R.A. the software tests the stability of the weight of the manger to decide if the weight is or is not disturbed by the animal. A series of at least 20 measurements are recorded on each manger every 10 seconds. The series are rejected as unstable if the standard deviation of the series exceeds a first preset threshold. If the series are not rejected the mean weight is compared with the previous recorded one and stored if the difference is greater than a second preset threshold value. The number of measurements in the series and the values of the thresholds have to be adjusted according the kinds of animals and forages used in the trial.

5.3.2.2. *Following the rate of intake during the meal: motivation to eat and satiation process.* Continuous recording of the weight of the manger allows the rate of intake to be followed during the different meals. During the meal, the rate of intake is highest at the beginning and then decreases continuously (satiation process) until satiety (Faverdin *et al.*, 1995). Simple models fit with accuracy cumulative intake during meals in both monogastrics and ruminants (Davis *et al.*, 1978; Faverdin, 1985; Baumont *et al.*, 1989):

$$DMI = (IRI/b) \times (1 - \exp(-bt)),\tag{5.3}$$

where DMI is dry matter intake of forage, IRI is the initial rate of intake, b is a constant of deceleration per unit of time and t is the time (Figure 5.4). When sheep have finished a first meal and the same hay is distributed again, initial rates of intake are similar for both meals, but constants of deceleration are higher during the second meal

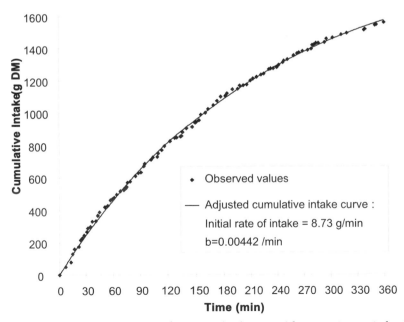

*Figure 5.4 Mathematical fitted cumulative intake during a 6 hours eating period calculated using equation (5.3). Data are recorded in sheep having access during 6 hours to lucerne hay offered ad libitum (Baumont, unpublished).*

than during the first one (Baumont *et al.*, 1990). Initial rate of intake may thus be a good criterion for evaluating the appetite for or the motivation to eat a given forage which comprises its palatability and prehensibility as it was shown that animals generally prefer feeds they can eat faster (Kenney and Black, 1984). The constant of deceleration may represent the satiation process, which happens logically more quickly during the second meal, animals being partially satiated from the first meal.

To assess the motivation to eat the satiation process can help to give a better understanding of intake regulation of different forages fed to the same animal. The higher initial rate of intake of lucerne hay compared to meadow hay (Baumont *et al.*, 1989) indicates its higher palatability together with a higher voluntary intake. The higher constant of deceleration measured with lucerne indicates a faster satiation process which can be related to a faster release of nutrients in agreement with a higher rate of digestion. Modelling kinetics of intake can also help to understand differences in intake regulation in relation to the physiological state of animals. In dairy cows fed the same diet, the initial rate of intake reflects the increase in motivation to eat with the advance of lactation (Faverdin, 1985). Modelling kinetics of intake was also successfully achieved in goats when simulating their browsing behaviour indoors with artificial shrubs (Meuret, 1989).

Rate of intake, especially at the beginning of a meal, seems to be a key factor in understanding variations in voluntary intake. Moseley and Antuna-Manendez (1989) found a high correlation between initial rate of intake and daily voluntary intake. Initial rate of intake express the motivation to eat a given forage and integrates sensory and nutritive properties of the feed that animals have learned from previous experiences (see review by Provenza, 1995).

### 5.3.3 Simulation of grazing behaviour

Analytical studies of intake and ingestive behaviour of animals fed indoors with cut forages allows the isolation of the role of the nutritive quality, its sensory properties and the effects of physical factors like particle size. However, it is well known that ingestive behaviour and thus, intake during grazing, is dependent on sward characteristics like height and density of herbage and spatial distribution of the plants. Unfortunately, under field conditions it is extremely difficult to isolate the independent effects of these different sward characteristics and, therefore, attempts have been made to develop procedures aimed at simulating grazing behaviour under controlled conditions.

5.3.3.1 *Artificial sward boards.* Indoor study of grazing behaviour was performed with cut turfs of well controlled height offered to cattle (Hughes *et al.*, 1991) or to sheep (Mursan *et al.*, 1989). Different plant species can also be grown in trays and offered to animals (Cosgrove and Mitchell, 1995). These techniques permit the measurement of ingestive behaviour with a level of detail that cannot be achieved in the field, but complete control over sward characteristics can only be obtained by hand-constructed swards (Black and Kenney,1984). Artificial pastures are prepared by fixing tillers from plants in holes that are drilled in wooden boards. The holes are spaced in rows from

10 to 50 mm apart, and with one, two or three tillers per hole. Grass height is varied by pulling tillers different distances through the holes. Thus, the height, the density and the spatial arrangement of the sward can easily be set by the experimenter. The use of hand-constructed swards was adapted by Spalinger *et al.* (1988) to study the foraging behaviour of browsing deer and by Laca *et al.* (1992a) to study cattle behaviour. This latter methodology integrates an improved hand-constructed sward with video and sound analysis for precise monitoring of grazing behaviour. The hand-constructed swards consisted of a series of small modules attached to a larger base board (Figure 5.5), each module being prepared as described by Black and Kenney (1984). Ingestive behaviour can be recorded very accurately during short experimental grazing sessions. The mass of herbage removed can be calculated as the product of the number of tiller holes grazed and the initial mass per tiller hole, minus the residual mass of tiller holes grazed. Bite area and bite depth can be precisely measured by counting and measuring the residual height of grazed plant parts. Bites and mastications can be identified and counted from the soundtrack of video tapes. Bite weight can be calculated by dividing mass of herbage removed by the number of bites taken. Grazing time is estimated as the time until all material is swallowed minus idling time and

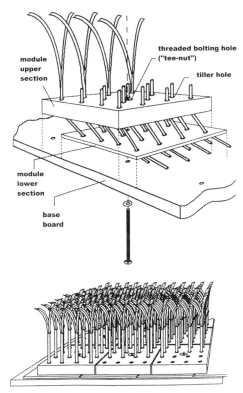

*Figure 5.5 Detail of an hand-constructed sward and module with herbage being clamped between two sections (Laca et al., 1992a).*

instantaneous intake rate is estimated as the dry matter removal divided by grazing time. In addition, an option was developed for recording the forces exerted on the herbage by the grazing animal.

Preparing hand constructed swards is time consuming as it takes about 1 hr for four people to prepare a sward of 54 modules (Laca et al., 1992a). Usually, measurements started 4 hours after herbage collection, but the willingness with which animals grazed the hand-constructed swards gave no indication that the interval from cutting or the handling of herbage modified grazing behaviour. Therefore, the methodology of artificial sward boards is of great interest for detailed analytical studies of the effects of sward characteristics on grazing behaviour (Laca et al., 1992b; Flores et al., 1993). Nevertheless Laca et al. (1992a) pointed out some differences between grazing hand-constructed swards and field grazing that may prevent the extrapolation of the results obtained with artificial swards to the grazing situation:

i.    Animals are not continuously at pasture when working with artificial swards.
ii.   The short duration of grazing sessions may introduce sources of bias.
iii.  The degree of depletion is controlled with artificial sward boards, in the field it is the result of grazing behaviour and is influenced by the grazing system and animal density.
iv.   Animals in field grazing situations are able to walk across the sward and search over relatively large areas and this may modify their behaviour.
v.    The proximity of other animals may affect behaviour under field conditions.

5.3.3.2 *Simulation of patch choice: learning procedures.* Artificial sward boards are designed to study grazing behaviour at the smallest scale of time and space. But a comprehensive model of grazing behaviour needs to distinguish different time and space scales as animals during grazing move from one patch to another patch, or feeding station, before a patch is completely depleted (Demment et al., 1995) and rules that govern patch choice need to be better understood. Learning the spatial structure of the pasture and thus of the accessibility to the different plants probably plays an important role. However, it is difficult to conduct, at pasture, critical studies of the way the preferences of animals varies with forage accessibility.

Operant procedures in which animals were taught to press plates with their muzzle to be rewarded with food were used to study preferences in ruminants (Mathews, 1983). More recently Dumont and Petit (1995) developed a learning procedure to study the choices of sheep and cattle between a good quality forage offered in limited quantities and a poor quality one available *ad libitum*. When an animal enters the test area, it can eat the poor quality forage in a manger or walk and be rewarded with a bucket of good quality forage. After animals have been trained to the test procedure, the effects of forage availability and accessibility can be studied by varying the amount of reward the animals receive and the distance they have to walk. Results of indoor preferences were compared with choices of the same animals between vegetative and reproductive patches at pasture. Mean responses of sheep and cattle were consistent at pasture with indoor measurements. However, no relationship was found between individual preferences in the two sets of measurements. Thus, the method can be used to infer general rules on the way animals forage at pasture, but does not allow the selection of individual animals for their grazing behaviour.

## 5.4 THE USE OF MEASUREMENTS OF HERBAGE INTAKE MADE INDOORS TO ESTIMATE INTAKE AND BEHAVIOUR BY THE GRAZING ANIMAL

The measurement of intake of a fresh herbage made indoors can be a useful guide to the total amount which can be voluntary consumed by the animal. It can also be used for the comparison and classification of different herbages. However, the relationship between the intake of herbage fed indoors and the intake of the same herbage grazed *in situ* is much more complex as the amount consumed during grazing is affected by the sward structure (as detailed above), and also by the grazing pressure (the number of animals in relation to the amount of herbage available).

The relationship between quantity of grass available and quantity of grass consumed by ruminants at pasture can be considered as asymptotic (Hodgson, 1976). Curves (Figure 5.6) drawn for growing cattle (Marsh and Murdoch, 1974) show that the relationships between amounts consumed and amount offered is curvilinear up to values for amounts offered of 5-6 kg DM/100 live weight. It is therefore not possible to use a measure of the amount of herbage consumed indoors to give an estimate of the amount consumed by the grazing animal.

The feeding conditions of the grazing animal are very different from those of the indoor animal, mainly because more herbage selection occurs during grazing although this varies according to grazing pressure. The lower the stocking rate the greater the

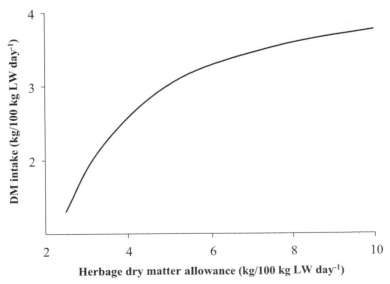

*Figure 5.6 Relationship between dry matter intake by steers at pasture and herbage dry matter allowance (Marsh and Murdoch, 1974).*

opportunity for the animal to be selective, i.e. to chose the most digestible or preferable plants or parts of plants, which results in a greater consumption of nutrients. Also at a given grazing pressure, selectively will be depend on the following:

- Stage of growth of herbage: selection will be less if the grass is young and leafy (Greenhalgh and Runcie, 1962) because the morphological composition of the plants is more uniform. Differences in digestibility between the various parts of the plant are smaller at the leafy stage of growth (Demarquilly and Chenost, 1969; Chenost et al., 1970), than later when lignification of the stems is rapid (Jarrige and Minson, 1964).
- Type of pasture: selection will be limited in the case of a homogenous canopy, possibilities of selection being smaller in pure swards than in mixed swards.
- Animal species: sheep have a greater ability to select than cattle; this ability is particular important in the case of a less dense and less green canopy (Dudzinski and Arnold, 1973).

However, when conditions of pasture utilization are such that grazing pressure is relatively high but intake is not restricted (percentage of refusals higher than that allowed indoors, but within the same order of magnitude), the intake in grazing conditions seems to be similar to that observed indoors. This is shown by the results of Greenhalgh and Runcie (1962) and by Greenhalgh et al. (1972) (Table 5.7). The herbage intake by dairy cows and growing cattle either at pasture (strip or rotational grazing) or zero grazed were of the same magnitude, where herbage allowance and stocking rates were similar in the two cases.

These results are confirmed by those of Demarquilly (1963, 1966) who observed that milk production and milk composition for housed cows, fed on grass, showed the same variation as grazing cows fed on the same grass, but milk production was lower for cows fed indoors than for grazing cows. Measurements of the amount of grass consumed indoors is thus likely to be an underestimate of that consumed at pasture.

It is possible to use values of the amounts consumed indoors to estimate the relative amounts consumed by grazing animals. It is also possible to examine by this method variation which occur for grass species, botanical composition, stage of utilization, age of herbage, number of cuts, season etc. The amount consumed indoors on occasions may be higher than that consumed at grazing in the case of plants whose intake at pasture can be limited by the presence of awns, spines, and by growth habit and plant texture. For example, tall fescue is consumed more easily when chopped and fed indoors than when grazed.

Finally, measurements made indoors have little or no value when the grazing animal can be selective, which is the case when it grazes range, natural pastures, savannahs etc.

*Table 5.7. Quantities of herbage consumed (kg OM day-1) by dairy cows and growing cattle either strip grazed or zero-grazed, at similar stocking rates and herbage allowances.*

(a) dairy cows - mixed sward of cocksfoot, perennial ryegrass, white and red clover (Greenhalgh and Runcie, 1962)

| Cut no | Strip grazing (allowance for maximum intake) | Zero grazing (refusal about 20%) |
|---|---|---|
| 1 | 12.2 | 12.5 |
| 2 | 12.4 | 11.6 |
| 3 | 13.3 | 13.5 |
| 4 | 12.9 | 12.1 |
| 5 | 13.2 | 12.3 |
| Mean | 12.8 | 12.4 |

(b) growing cattle - pure perennial ryegrass (Greenhalgh *et al.*, 1972)

| Cut no | Rotational grazing (C)[*] | (V)[*] | Zero grazing (Z)[*] |
|---|---|---|---|
| 1 | 7.03 | 7.39 | 6.42 |
| 2 | 5.50 | 6.59 | 7.20 |
| 3 | 6.50 | 6.87 | 6.13 |
| 4 | 5.15 | 6.30 | 6.18 |
| Mean | 6.18 | 6.87 | 6.54 |

* (C) (Z) = same stocking rate
(V) = stocking rate continuously varied to give the same liveweight gain per animal as group Z.

## 5.5 REFERENCES

ABRAMS S.M., HARPSTER H.W., WANGNESS P.I., SHENK J.S., KECK E. AND ROSENBERGER JL (1987) Use of a standard forage to reduce effects of animal variation on estimates of mean voluntary intake. *Journal of Dairy Science*, **70**, 1235-1240

BAILE C.A. (1975) Control of feed intake in ruminants. In: McDonald I.W. AND Warner A.C.I (eds.) *Digestion and metabolism in the ruminants.* pp. 333-350

BALCH C.C. (1958) Observations on the act of eating in cattle. *British Journal of Nutrition,* **12**, 330-345

BAUMONT R., DULPHY J.P. AND ANDRIEU J.P. (1988) Comportement alimentaire et état de réplétion du réticulo-rumen chez le mouton nourri à volonté de foin de prairie ou de luzerne, avec accès continu ou limité: incidences sur le contrôle physique de l'ingestion. *Reproduction Nutrition Développement,* **28**, 573-588

BAUMONT R. (1989) Etat de réplétion du réticulo-rumen et ingestion des fourrages: Incidences sur le contrôle à court-terme de la quantité de foin ingérée par le mouton. *Thèse de Doctorat INA-PG* 159 pp.

BAUMONT R. AND BRUN J.P. (1992) Enregistrement et analyse du profil d'ingestion et de rumination chez le bovin. *In: 2e Journées de la mesure INRA Clermont-Ferrand.*

BAUMONT R., BRUN J.P. AND DULPHY J.P. (1989) Influence of the nature of hay on its ingestibility and the kinetics of intake during large meals in sheep and cow. In: JARRIGE R. (ed.) *XVIth International Grassland Congress, Nice, France.(2)* French Grassland Society, pp. 787-788

BAUMONT R., SEGUIER N. AND DULPHY J.P. (1990) Rumen fill, forage palatability and alimentary behaviour in sheep. *Journal of Agricultural Science (Cambridge), 115*, 277-284

BAUMONT R., VIMAL T. AND DÉTOUR A. (1998) An automatic system to record and analyse kinetics of intake in sheep fed indoors with one or two feeds offered at the same time. *Proceedings of the IXth European Intake Workshop.* Institute of Grassland and Environmental Research North Wyke. November 1988, pp. 21-21.

BEAUCHEMIN K.A. AND BUCHANAN-SMITH J.G. (1989) Effects of dietary neutral detergent fiber concentration and supplementary long hay on chewing activities and milk production of dairy cows. *Journal of Dairy Science, 72*, 2288-2300

BEAUCHEMIN K.A., ZELIN S., GENNER D. AND BUCHANAN-SMITH J.G. (1989) An automatic system for quantification of eating and ruminating activities of dairy cattle housed in stalls. *Journal of Dairy Science, 72*, 2746-2759

BLACK J.L. AND KENNEY P.A. (1984) Factors affecting diet selection by sheep.2.Height and density of pasture. *Australian Journal of Agricultural Research, 35*, 565-578

BLAXTER K. L. AND WILSON R. S. (1962) The voluntary intake of roughages by steers. *Animal Production, 4*, 351-358.

BLAXTER K. L., WAINMAN F. W. AND WILSON R. S. (1961) The regulation of food intake by sheep. *Animal Production, 3*, 51-61.

BLAXTER K. L., WAINMAN F. W. AND DAVIDSON J. L. (1966) The voluntary intake of food by sheep and cattle in relation to their energy requirements for maintenance. *Animal Production, 8*, 75-83.

BRUN J.P., PRACHE S. AND BÉCHET G (1984) A portable device for eating behaviour studies. *5th Meeting European Grazing Workshop.*

BUCHMAN D. T. AND HEMKEN. R. W. (1964) *Ad libitum* intake and digestibility of several alfalfa hays by cattle and sheep. *Journal of Dairy Science, 47*, 861-864.

BURNS J.C., POND K.R. AND FISHER D.S. (1994) Measurement of forage intake. In: FAHEY G.C. (ed.) *Forage quality, evaluation and utilization.* pp 494-532

CAMMELL S. B. (1977) Equipment and techniques used for research into the intake and digestion of forages by sheep and calves. *Technical Report N°24, Grassland Research Institute, Hurley Maidenhead.*

CAMPBELL J. R. AND MERILAN C. P. (1961) Effect of frequency of feeding on production characteristics and feed utilization in lactating dairy cows. *Journal of Dairy cows, 44*, 664-671.

CHENOST M. AND DEMARQUILLY C. (1969) Comparaison entre le pâturage et l'affouragement en vert pour la production de viande bovine. *Annales de Zootechnie, 18*, 277-298.

CHENOST M., GRENET E., DEMARQUILLY C. AND JARRIGE R. (1970) The use of the nylon bag technique for the study digestion in the rumen and for predicting feed value. *Proceedings of the 11th International Grassland Congress*, pp. 697-701.

COLLINS D. P. (1973) Zero grazing of beef cattle. *An Foras Taluntais*, 35-36.

COSGROVE G.P., MITCHELL R.J. (1995) Effect of sward type on intake rate parameters during progressive sward defoliation by lambs. *Annales de Zootechnie*, **44**, 249.

CRAMPTON E. W., DONEFER F. AND LLOYD L. E. (1960) A nutritive value index for forages. *Journal of Animal Science*, **19**, 538-544.

DAVIS J.D., COLLINS B.J. AND LEVINE M.W. (1978) The interaction between gustatory stimulation and gut feedback in the control of the ingestion of liquid diets. In: BOOTH D.A. (ed.) *Hunger Models*. Academic Press, 109-143

DEMARQUILLY C. (1963) Influence de la nature du pâturage sur la production laitière et la composition du lait. *Annales de Zootechnie,* **12**, 69-104.

DEMARQUILLY C. (1966) Valeur alimentaire de l'herbe des prairies temporaires aux stades d'exploitation pour le pâturage. II - Quantité ingérée par les vaches laitières. *Annales de Zootechnie*, **15**, 147-169.

DEMARQUILLY C. (1970) Influence de la déshydratation à basse température sur la valeur alimentaire des fourrages. *Annales de Zootechnie*, **19**, 45-51.

DEMARQUILLY C. AND CHENOST M. (1969) Etude de la digestion de fourrages dans le rumen par la méthode des sachets de nylon. Liaisons avec la valeur alimentaire. *Annales de Zootechnie*, **18**, 419-436.

DEMARQUILLY C AND DULPHY J. P. (1977) Effect of ensiling on feed intake and animal performances. *Proceedings of the 1st International Meeting on Animal Production from Temperature Grassland, Dublin*, pp 53-61.

DEMARQUILLY C. AND WEISS Ph. (1970) Tableaux de la valeur alimentaire des fourrages. *Ministère de l'Agriculture, I.N.R.A. SEI, étude n° 42*, M3 Fourr, 53, Published Elsevier. pp. 311.

DEMARQUILLY C. AND WEISS Ph. (1971) Liaisons entre les quantités de matière sèche de fourrages verts ingérées par les moutons et celles ingérées par les bovins. *Annales de Zootechnie*, **20**, 119-134.

DEMARQUILLY C. AND ANDRIEU, J (1987) Digestibilité et ingestibilité des fourrages verts chez le mouton: effets respectifs du niveau d'alimentation et de l'âge ou du poids des animaux. *Reproduction Nutrition Développement*, 27, 281-282

DEMMENT M.W., PEYRAUD J.L., LACA E.A. (1995) Herbage intake at grazing: a modelling approach. In: JOURNET M., GRENET E., FARCE M.H., THÉRIEZ M. AND DEMARQUILLY C. (eds.) *Recent developments in the nutrition of herbivores. Proceedings of the IV$^{th}$ International Symposium on the Nutrition of Herbivores. Clermont-Ferrand 1995.* INRA Editions, 121-141

DOUGHERTY C.T., BRADLEY N.W., CORNELIUS P.L. AND LAURIAULT L.M. (1989) Ingestive behaviour of beef cattle offered different forms of lucerne (*Medicago sativa* L.). *Grass and Forage Science*, **44**, 335-342.

DUDZINSKI M. L. AND ARNOLD G W (1973) Comparison of diets of sheep and cattle grazing together on sown pastures on the southern tablelands of New South Wales by principal components analysis. *Australian Journal of Agricultural Research*, **24**, 899-912.

DULPHY J.P. AND DEMARQUILLY C. (1973) Influence de la machine de récolte et de la finesse de hachage sur la valeur alimentaire des ensilages. *Annales de Zootechnie,* **22**, 199-217.

DULPHY J.P. AND DEMARQUILLY C. (1994) The regulation and prediction of feed intake in ruminants in relation to feed characteristics. *Livestock Production Science,* **39**, 1-12

DULPHY J.P., ELMEDDAH Y. AND BAUMONT, R (1988) Influence du rythme de distribution sur les activités alimentaires et l'évolution journalière du contenu ruminal chez le mouton. *Reproduction Nutrition Développement,* **28**, 919-929

DULPHY J.P., FAVERDIN P. AND JARRIGE R. (1989) Feed intake: the fill unit systems. In: JARRIGE R. (ed.) *Ruminant Nutrition: Recommended allowances and feed tables, John Libbey Eurotext*, pp 61-71.

DULPHY J.P., RÉMOND B. AND THÉRIEZ M. (1980) Ingestive behaviour and related activities in ruminants. In: Y RUCKEBUSCH Y AND THIVEND P. (eds.) *Digestive Physiology and Metabolism in Ruminants* MTP Ltd Press, pp. 103-122

DUMONT B AND PETIT M. (1995) An indoor method for studying the preferences of sheep and cattle at pasture. *Applied Animal Behaviour Science,* **46**, 67-80

EVANS E.M. AND POTTER J.F (1984) The reproducibility of *in vivo* estimates of digestibility and voluntary digestible organic matter intake of grass varieties by sheep. *Grass and Forage Science,* **39**, 101-106

FAVERDIN P. (1985) Régulation de l'ingestion des vaches laitières en début de lactation. *Thèse Doct. Ing. I.N.A. - P.G.* 131 pp.

FAVERDIN P., BAUMONT R. AND INGVARTSEN K.L. (1995) Control and prediction of feed intake in ruminants. In: JOURNET M., GRENET E., MH FARCE M.H., THÉRIEZ M. AND DEMARQUILLY C. (eds.) *Recent developments in the nutrition of herbivores. Proceedings of the IV$^{th}$ International Symposium on the Nutrition of Herbivores. Clermont-Ferrand 1995* INRA Editions, 95-120

FLORES E.R., LACA E.A., GRIGGS T.C. AND DEMMENT M.W. (1993) Sward height and vertical morphological differentiation determine cattle bite dimensions. *Agronomy Journal,* **85**, 527-532

FORBES J.M. (1995) Feeding behaviour. *In: Voluntary Food Intake and Diet Selection in Farm Animals.* Published CAB International, pp 11-37

GRASSLAND RESEARCH INSTITUTE (1966) *Annual Report of the Grassland Research Institute, Hurley, Maidenhead 1966* pp. 41-42.

GREENHALGH J. F. D. AITKEN J. N. AND REID G. W. (1972) A note on the zero-grazing of beef cattle. *Journal of the British Grassland Society,* **27**, 173-177.

GREENHALGH J.F.D. AND RUNCIE K.V. (1962) The herbage intake and milk production of strip and zero grazed dairy cows. *Journal Agricultural Science Cambridge,* **59**, 95-103.

HEANEY D. P. (1979) Sheep as pilot animals. In: W J PIGDEN W.J., BALCH C.C. AND GRAHAM M. (eds.) *Proceedings of the Workshop on standardization of analytical methodology for feeds pp 45-48.* Ottawa 12-14 March 1979, IDRC - 134c.

HEANEY D. P., PIGDEN W. J. AND PRITCHARD G. I. (1966) The effect of freezing or drying pasture herbage on digestibility and voluntary intake assays with sheep. *Proceedings of the 10th International Grassland Congress,* Helsinki, Section 2, Paper 7.

HEANEY D. P., PRITCHARD G. I. AND PIGDEN W. J. (1968) Variability in *ad libitum* forage intake by sheep. *Journal of Animal Science,* **27**, 159-164.

HEINRICHS A.J., CONRAD H.R. (1987) Measuring feed intake patterns and meal size of lactating dairy cows. *Journal of Dairy Science,* **70**, 705-711

HODGSON J. (1976) Pasture utilization by the grazing animal, pp. 93 In: HODGSON J. AND JACKSON D.K. (eds.) *British Grassland Society Occasional Symposium, n° 8.* pp. 93.

HUGHES T.P., SYKES A.R., POPPI D.P. AND HODGSON, J (1991) The influence of sward structure on peak bite force and bite weight in sheep. *Proceedings of the New Zealand Society of Animal Production,* **51**, 153-158

HUTTON J. B. (1962) Studies on the nutritive value of New Zealand dairy pastures. II. Herbage intake and digestibility studies with dry cattle. *New Zealand Journal of Agricultural Research,* **5**, 409-424.

INGALLS J. R., THOMAS J. W. AND TESAR M. B. (1965) Comparison of responses to various forages by sheep, rabbits and heifers. *Journal of Animal Science,* **24**, 1165-1168.

INRA. Département d'Elevage des Ruminants (1979) Le système des unités d'encombrement pour les bovins. *Bulletin Techique de Theix,* **38**, 57-79.

JARRIGE R. AND MINSON D J (1964) Digestibilité des constituants du ray-grass anglais 24 et du dactyle S37, plus spécialement des constituants glucidiques. *Annales de Zootechnie*, **13**, 117-150.

JARRIGE R., DEMARQUILLY C., DULPHY J.P., HODEN A., JOURNET M., BERANGER C. GEAY Y., MALTERRE C., PETIT M. AND ROBELIN J. (1979) Le système des unités d'encombrement pour les bovins. *Bulletin Techique de Theix*, **38**, 57-79

JARRIGE R., DEMARQUILLY C., DULPHY J.P., HODEN A., ROBELIN J., BÉRANGER C., GEAY Y., JOURNET M., MALTERRE C., MICOL D. AND PETIT M. (1986) The INRA "Fill Unit" system for predicting the voluntary intake of forage-based diets in ruminants: a review. *Journal of Animal Science*, **63**, 1737-1758

JARRIGE R., DEMARQUILLY C., JOURNET., M. AND BERANGER C. (1973) The nutritive value of processed dehydrated forages with special reference to the influence of physical form and particle size. *In: Proceedings of the First international green crop drying Congress*. pp. 99-118

JARRIGE R., DULPHY J.P., FAVERDIN P., BAUMONT R. AND DEMARQUILLY C. (1995) Activités d'ingestion et de rumination. In: JARRIGE R., Y RUCKEBUSCH Y., DEMARQUILLY C., FARCE M.H. AND JOURNETM. (eds.) *Nutrition des Ruminants Domestiques* INRA, pp. 123-181

JONES R AND FORBES J.M. (1984) A note on effects of glyphosphate and quinine on the palatability of hay for sheep. *Animal Production*, **38**, 301-303

KENNEY P.A. AND BLACK J.L. (1984) Factors affecting diet selection by sheep. I. Potential intake rate and acceptability of feed. *Australian Journal of Agricultural Research*, **35**, 551-563

KLEIBER M. (1965) Metabolic body size. In: K L BLAXTER K.L. (ed.) *3rd Symposium of Energy Metabolism*, pp 427-435. London, New York, Academic Press.

LACA E.A., UNGAR E.D., SELIGMAN N.G AND DEMMENT M.W. (1992b) Effect of sward height and bulk density on bite dimensions of cattle grazing homogeneous swards. *Grass and Forage Science*, **47**, 91-102

LACA E.A., UNGAR E.D., SELIGMAN N.G., RAMEY M.R. AND DEMMENT M.W. (1992a) An integrated methodology for studying short-term grazing behaviour of cattle. *Grass and Forage Science*, **47**, 81-90

LOFGREEN G.P., MEYER J.H. AND HULL J.L. (1957) Behaviour patterns of sheep and cattle being fed pasture or silage. *Journal of Animal Science*, **16**, 773-780

LUGINBUHL J.M. POND K.R., RUSS J.C. AND BURNS J.C. (1987) A simple electronic device and computer interface system for monitoring chewing behavior of stall-fed ruminant animals. *Journal of Dairy Science*, **70 (6)**, 1307-1312

Mac RAE J. C., CAMPBELL D. R. AND EADIE J. (1975) Changes in the biochemical composition of herbage upon freezing and thawing. *Journal of Agricultural Science, Cambridge*, **84**, 125-131.

MARSH R. AND MURDOCH J. C. (1974) Effect of high fertilizer nitrogen and stocking rate on liveweight gain per animal and per hectare. *Journal of the British Grassland Society*, **29**, 305-313.

MATTHEWS L.R. (1983) Measurement and scaling of food preferences in dairy cows: concurrent schedule and free-access techniques. *PhD. University of Waikato*, 236 pp.

MEIJS J. A. C. (1979) Advances in the direct techniques to estimate herbage intake. *European Grazing workshop, 2-5 April 1979, Lelystad*.

METZ J.H.M. (1975) Time patterns of feeding and rumination in domestic cattle. *Mededelingen Landbouwhogeschool Wageningen*, **75**, 1-66

MEURET. M (1989) Valorisation par des caprins laitiers de rations ligneuses prélevées sur parcours: feuillages, fromages et flux ingérés. *Thèse de Doctorat en Sciences Agronomiques, Faculté des Sciences Agronomiques de Gembloux*, 229 pp.

MICHALET-DOREAU B. AND GATEL F. (1983) Evolution au cours d'une année des quantités de foin ingérées par des béliers castrés. *Annales de Zootechnie*, **32**, 459-464

MICHALET-DOREAU B. AND GATEL. F (1983) Evolution au cours d'une année des quantités de foin ingérées par des béliers castrés. *Annales de Zootechnie*, **37**, 151-158

MINSON D. J. (1966). The intake and nutritive value of fresh, frozen and dried *sorghum almum, Digitaria decumbens, and Panicum maximum. Journal of the British Grassland Society,* **21**, 123-126.

MINSON D. J., HARRIS C. E., RAYMOND W. F. AND MILFORD R. (1964) The digestibility and voluntary intake of S 22 and H 1 rye grass, S 170 tall fescue, S 48 timothy, S 215 meadow fescue and germinal cocksfoot. *Journal of the British Grassland Society,* **19**, 298-305.

MINSON D. J., STOBBS T. H., HEGARTY M. P. ANDPLAYNE M. J. (1976) Measuring the nutritive value of pasture plants. *Tropical Pasture Research, Principles and Methods. Bulletin 51, Chapter 13, Commonwealth Agricultural Bureaux.*

MOSELEY G. AND ANTUNA MANENDEZ A. (1989) Factors affecting the eating rate of forage feeds. In: JARRIGE R. (ed.) *XVIth International Grassland Congress, Nice, France.* Published French Grassland Society, pp 789-790

MURSAN A., HUGHES T.P., NICOL A.M. AND SUGIURA T. (1989) The influence of sward height on the mechanics of grazing in steers and bulls. *Proceedings of the New Zealand Society of Animal Production,* **49**, 233-236

PENNING P.D. (1983) A technique to record automatically some aspects of grazing and ruminating behaviour in sheep. *Grass and Forage Science,* **38**, 89-96

PENNING P.D., STEEL G.L. AND JOHNSON, R.H. (1984) Further development and use of an automatic recording system in sheep grazing studies. *Grass and Forage Science,* **39**, 345-351

PIGDEN W. J., PRITCHARD G. I., WINTER K. A. AND LOGAN U. S. (1961) Freezing - a technique for forage investigations. *Journal of Animal Science,* **4**, 796-801.

PROVENZA F.D. (1995) Role of learning in food preferences of ruminants: Greenhalgh and Reid revisited. In: ENGELHARDT W.V., LEONHARD-MAREK S., BREVES G. AND GIESECKE D. (eds.) *Ruminant physiology: digestion, metabolism, growth and reproduction. Proceedings of the Eighth International Symposium on Ruminant Physiology.* Ferdinand Enke Verlag, pp 233-247

PUTNAM, PA, LEHMAN, R, LUBER, W (1968) Diurnal rates of feed intake by steers in drylot. *Journal of Animal Science,* **27**, 1494-1496.

RAYMOND, W F, HARRIS, C E and PARKER, V G (1953) Studies on the digestibility of herbage. II. Effect of freezing and cold storage of herbage on its digestibility by sheep. *Journal of the British Grassland Society,* **8**, 315-320.

RUCKEBUSCH, Y (1963) Recherches sur la régulation centrale du comportement alimentaire chez les ruminants. *Thèse de Doctorat en Sciences Naturelles, Université de Lyon*, 213 p

SPALINGER D.E., HANLEY T.A. AND ROBBINS C.T. (1988) Analysis of the functional response in foraging in the Sitka black-tailed deer. *Ecology*, **69**, 1166-1175.

STRIKLIN W.R., WILSON L.L. AND GRAVES H.B. (1976) Feeding behavior of angus and Charolais-Angus cows during summer and winter. Journal of Animal Science, **43**, 721-732

SUZUKI S., FUJITA H. AND SHINDE Y (1969) Change in the rate of eating during a meal and the effect of the interval between meals on the rate at which cows eat roughages. *Animal Production,* **11**, 29-41

TAYLER J. C. AND RUDMAN J. E. (1965) Height and method of cutting or grazing in relation to herbage consumption and liveweight gain. *Proceeding of the 9th International Grassland Congress, Sao Paulo,* **20**, pp. 1639-1644.

THOMPSON J.M., PARKS J.R. AND PERY D. (1985) Food intake, growth and body composition in Australian Merino Sheep selected for high and low weaning weight. 1- Food intake, food efficiency and growth. *Animal Production*, **40**, 55-70.

VAN ES A. J. H. AND VAN DER HONING Y. (1976) Energy and nitrogen balances of lactating cows fed fresh or frozen grass in Energy Metabolism of Farm Animals, pp38. *Proceedings of the 7th Symposium EAAP, Vichy, France, September 1976.*

VERITE R. AND JOURNET M. (1970) Influence de la teneur en eau et de la déshydratation de l'herbe sur sa valeur alimentaire pour les vaches laitières. *Annales de Zootechnie*, **19**, 255-268.

ZEMMELINCK G. (1980) Effect of selective consumption on voluntary intake and digestibility of tropical forages. *Agricultural Research Report 896, Centre for Agricultural Publishing and Documentation, Pudoc, Wageningen.*

# CHAPTER 6

# INGESTIVE BEHAVIOUR

**P. D. Penning and S. M. Rutter**

## 6.1 INTRODUCTION

Many of the approaches and methods described in the first edition of this book are still relevant today and remain unaltered in this chapter. However, the section on experimental variation has been omitted, as this topic has been dealt with in Chapter 7. Considerable advances in the recording of behaviour have been made over the last 17 years and, these developments and improvements in techniques that permit automatic detailed recording of grazing behaviour, have led to major advances in our understanding of the grazing process.

Throughout this chapter the terminology used is based on the definitions given by Gibb (1996). The daily consumption of herbage by a grazing animal (I g/d) can be viewed as the product of total grazing time (GT, min) and intake rate (IR g/min grazing). IR (g/min) is the product of biting rate (BR/min) and bite mass (BM g/bite). Penning *et al.* (1991a, 1994) have shown how BM is related to sward state and Parsons *et al.* (1994a) and Newman *et al.* (1994a) have shown how BM controls BR. A simple model of intake (Allden and Whittaker, 1970) may be written as:

$$I = GT \times IR \tag{6.1}$$

Where:

GT = Meal Duration x No. Meals                                (6.2)

IR = BM x BR                                                   (6.3)

Relationships between BM and sward state are illustrated in Figure 6.1. This chapter deals mainly with ingestive behaviour of domesticated ruminants, however,

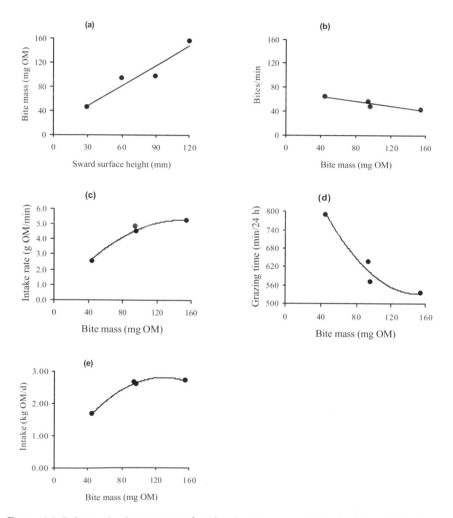

*Figure 6.1. Relationship between sward surface height (mm) and bite mass (mg OM/bite) (a) and relationships between bite mass (mg OM/bite) and biting rate (bite/min) (b), intake rate (g OM/min) (c), grazing time (min/24h) (d) and daily intake (kg OM) (e). Measured with lactating ewes (Penning et al., 1991a).*

some aspects of behaviour associated with the grazing process such as locomotion and rumination will be considered briefly. It is beyond the scope of this chapter to cover other aspects of animal behaviour and, for a more general understanding of the subject, readers are referred to Gordon (1995) and books on cattle behaviour by Phillips (1993) and on sheep behaviour by Rutter (2002) and Lynch *et al.* (1992).

Behaviour exhibited by animals is an indication of the relationship between their internal state (i.e. nutritional requirements, health, etc.) and their environment (i.e. sward state, climate, etc.). Thus, a knowledge of grazing behaviour can help to explain the results from experiments and, the aspects of behaviour that need to be recorded, will depend on the objectives of these experiments. However, before setting out experimental protocols and adopting techniques to record grazing behaviour, it is necessary to have a general understanding of the grazing process; this is first discussed in this chapter before detailed methods of recording behaviour are described.

## 6.2 DESCRIPTION OF THE GRAZING PROCESS

Grazing animals are surrounded by their food source, the pasture, and are presented with a great variety of choices when eating, i.e. which plants to consume, whether to select leaves, flowers, live or dead material. The animals also trample, defecate, urinate and lie on the pasture. All these activities, which are part of the grazing process, affect sward state which in turn affects feeding behaviour. Thus, a dynamic relationship exists between the sward and the grazer. The animals spend their day eating, ruminating, drinking and in other activities such as resting, social interactions and reproductive activities. Typical examples of some of these behaviours are presented in Figure 6.2. These patterns have been shown to repeat at 24 h intervals but may be modified by weather conditions (Champion *et al.*, 1994). Grazing time will be affected by the physiological state of the animals and the pasture (Penning *et al.*, 1995). Under temperate conditions where animals are allowed to graze for 24h of each

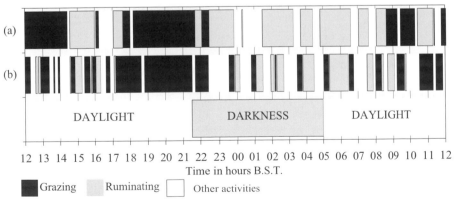

*Figure 6.2. Typical diurnal patterns of grazing, ruminating and idling activity in (a) dairy heifers grazing ryegrass and (b) ewes grazing adjacent monocultures of white clover and ryegrass in summer.*

day, the main grazing bout occurs in the evening and terminates with the onset of darkness. This evening feeding bout may last for several hours and up to 48% of the daily GT may be concentrated in this period (Penning *et al.*, 1991b). These patterns of grazing activity are important considerations when formulating intermittent sampling protocols.

How animals eat is also a complex process. Gibb (1996) draws the distinction here between time spent eating and grazing, where eating time is grazing time excluding intra-meal intervals. Animals gather and manipulate herbage in the sward with their tongues (cattle) and lips (sheep and goats), grip the herbage between their incisors and the upper dental pad and severe it from the sward (bite) often, but not invariably, with a jerk of the head. The herbage severed by the bite is then manipulated, chewed (mastication) and formed into a bolus before it is swallowed. Biting and masticating jaw movements appear to be mutually exclusive in sheep (Penning 1986; Penning *et al.*, 1991a) but in cattle these activities may be carried out simultaneously as 'chew bites' (Laca and Wallis DeFries 2000). Some examples of the relationships between biting and non-biting jaw movements for cows and ewes are given in Table 6.1.

There is an upper limit to the rate of jaw movements in grazing animals and, for sheep, this rate is fairly constant at about 160 min$^{-1}$ (i.e. the time required for the sheep to open and close its jaws is about 0.4 s). These jaw movements have to be allocated between biting and non-biting jaw movements. As bite mass increases non-biting jaw movements also increase and, therefore, time available for biting decreases. For cattle this control mechanism is different because, as stated previously, biting and 'chewing' do not appear to be mutually exclusive. These mechanisms have been modelled in

*Table 6.1. Grazing behaviour of lactating dairy cows (a) and lactating ewes (b) grazing continuously stocked ryegrass swards at different Sward Surface Heights. (Gibb et al., 1999 and Penning et al., 1994).*

|  | Sward surface height (cm) | | |
| --- | --- | --- | --- |
| (a) | 5 | 7 | 9 |
| Eating time (min 24 h$^{-1}$) | 607 | 583 | 528 |
| Biting rate (bites min$^{-1}$) | 63 | 59 | 59 |
| Non-biting grazing jaw movements (min$^{-1}$) | 19 | 19 | 18 |
| Total grazing jaw movements (min$^{-1}$) | 81 | 78 | 76 |
| (b) | 3 | 6 | 9 |
| Eating time (min 24 h$^{-1}$) | 763 | 686 | 666 |
| Biting rate (bites min$^{-1}$) | 76 | 71 | 69 |
| Non-biting grazing jaw movements (min$^{-1}$) | 85 | 89 | 94 |
| Total grazing jaw movements (min$^{-1}$) | 161 | 161 | 163 |

detail by Spalinger and Hobbs (1992), Parsons *et al.* (1994a) and Newman *et al.* (1995) and offer a mechanistic explanation of the relationship between sward state, jaw movements and intake rate. Obviously, from the above, recording and distinguishing between types of jaw movements whilst animals are grazing is an important step towards understanding ingestive behaviour. For example, if all jaw movements were to be counted as bites, and used in the calculation of bite mass, then bite mass would be greatly underestimated. However, it is extremely difficult to make these observations manually and continuous recording of more than one animal, simultaneously, is impossible for one observer. Thus, sampling of behaviour at intervals in time will have to be used or automatic recording systems employed. Strict definitions of eating, grazing and jaw movement types will be required before observations are carried out and these must be consistently applied throughout behavioural measurements. Rates of jaw movements have also been shown to vary with time of day (Champion *et al.*, 1994, Orr *et al.*, 1997 and Gibb *et al.*, 1998) and so sampling times should be designed to take this variation into account.

Ruminating, i.e. the regurgitation of a bolus of food from the rumen that is chewed and then swallowed, is another important activity as shown in Figure 6.2. Although ruminating *per se* does not affect intake rate directly, the requirement to ruminate may reduce time available for grazing and thus affect total intake. Ruminating is often difficult to observe as it occurs mainly during the night when animals are lying resting, in fact Ruckebusch (1975), has shown that, in cattle and sheep, slow wave sleep and ruminating are associated.

6.2.1 Grazing time (GT) and eating time

Estimates of grazing time may be derived from continuous monitoring or by sampling the activity at intervals. The former is more accurate but, as already discussed, is difficult to carry out unless automatic recording systems are utilised. When behaviour is recorded at intervals, it is assumed that each record is representative of the behaviour over the time interval since the previous recording.

Grazing time has already been defined as: *number of meals x meal duration* (Equation 6.2). GT may be divided into bouts ('meals') but this requires continuous recording or very frequent sampling intervals (1 min or less). There are various mathematical methods for dividing behaviour into bouts (Metz, 1975, Forbes *et al.*, 1986 and Sibley *et al.*, 1990) but these methods have recently been criticised by Tolkamp *et al.*, (1998) who suggested an alternative method of calculation. Basically, the pauses measured during grazing activity are divided into two populations *inter-* and *intra*-meal intervals and the minimum length of an *inter*-meal interval is calculated (bout criterion) which is then used to split grazing time into 'meals'.

Eating time (already defined as GT minus intra-meal intervals) is almost impossible to record manually as some intra-meal intervals are very short, but it can be recorded by some automatic systems. In estimating daily intake from IR measured over a short period multiplied by eating time rather than GT, gives a more accurate estimate of daily intake. This will be discussed in more detail later in Chapter 3.

## 6.2.2 Biting rate (BR)

The mean biting rate over 24 h may be calculated from the total bites divided by total grazing time. Realistically, total bites can only be counted using an automatic system. BR is normally measured over short periods of time often at intervals during the day and sampling intervals should be planned carefully to take into account the diurnal variation in jaw movements (Table 6.2). BR tends to be higher in the evening for cows and lower in the evening for sheep whilst total grazing jaw movements tend to be higher in the evening for both cattle and sheep.

Biting rate during grazing may be estimated by counting the number of bites in a given grazing period. As well as the time spent biting, grazing may included periods when then animal is actively seeking herbage to bite or is chewing herbage it has just harvested from the sward. Some critical value for a period of time when none of these activities is taking place should be set in order to decide when grazing has stopped. In the automatic recording system of Penning et al., (1984) this is set at >30 s in any minute. However, there are no hard and fast rules and experimenters will have to decide for themselves appropriate values to adopt.

An alternative approach to estimating biting rate, is to record the time taken for a specific number of bites to be taken. In both these methods measurements should be repeated several times in each observation period and used to calculate a mean.

## 6.2.3 Total grazing bites

The total number of grazing bites over 24 h or some shorter interval of time may be measured directly, or calculated as the product of grazing time (GT) and the mean biting rate (BR) over time. The former approach is difficult unless automatic recording techniques are used and, from Table 6.1, it can be calculated that cattle took approximately 40,000 and sheep 60,000 bites per day. Both manual and automatic recording techniques may be used for the sampling method, but it is important to ensure that criteria for determining grazing activity and estimating biting rate are compatible.

## 6.2.4 Intake rate (IR) and bite mass (BM)

The rate of herbage intake (weight per unit time) may be calculated as a daily average value from estimates of daily herbage intake (I) divided by daily grazing time (GT), or measured directly over short periods of time. Estimates of BM are obtained by dividing intake by the number of bites recorded over the appropriate time interval. The procedures for measuring grazing time and biting rate or total bites have already been discussed in general terms. The additional procedures necessary for the estimation of rate of intake and intake per bite are outlined here.

6.2.4.1 *Calculation from estimates of daily herbage intake, grazing time and total bites.* Estimates of rate of intake per minute (IR) and bite mass (BM) made using these procedures are susceptible to the cumulative errors of the estimation of the variables used in the calculations (Equations 6.1 to 6.3). Calculation of IR and BM in this way involves least direct interference with experimental animals and is convenient when intake and behaviour measurements are already available. However, this method will only give estimates of **mean** IR and BM over 24 h. Table 6.2 shows clearly how IR and BM vary over the day. Thus, unless total bites are counted over a 24 h period, estimating mean BR from sampling at different times of the day, presents problems (Table 6.2) and may give rise to errors in the estimate of mean BM.

*Table 6.2. The effect of time of day on grazing jaw movements and intake characteristics of ryegrass swards grazed by (a) lactating cows and (b) dry ewes at 6.5 and 6 cm sward surface height, respectively (Gibb et al., 1998, Orr et al., 1997), measured over 1 h.*

| | Time of day (h) | | | |
|---|---|---|---|---|
| (a) | 07.00 | 11.30 | 16.00 | 19.00 |
| Bites (min$^{-1}$) | 53 | 48 | 52 | 59 |
| Non-biting grazing jaw movements (min$^{-1}$) | 25 | 32 | 25 | 21 |
| Total grazing jaw movements (min$^{-1}$) | 77 | 79 | 77 | 81 |
| Bite mass (fresh matter mg bite$^{-1}$) | 1623 | 1187 | 1304 | 1215 |
| Bite mass (DM mg bite$^{-1}$) | 332 | 348 | 481 | 402 |
| Intake rate (fresh matter g min$^{-1}$ eating) | 83.2 | 55.3 | 66.2 | 69.4 |
| Intake rate (DM g min$^{-1}$ eating) | 17.1 | 18.0 | 24.0 | 23.0 |
| (b) | 07.30 | 11.30 | 15.30 | 19.00 |
| Bites (min$^{-1}$) | 85 | 66 | 68 | 68 |
| Non-biting grazing jaw movements (min$^{-1}$) | 71 | 86 | 87 | 90 |
| Total grazing jaw movements (min$^{-1}$) | 156 | 152 | 155 | 157 |
| Bite mass (fresh matter mg bite$^{-1}$) | 200 | 152 | 206 | 191 |
| Bite mass (DM mg bite$^{-1}$) | 30 | 38 | 53 | 51 |
| Intake rate (fresh matter g min$^{-1}$ eating) | 17 | 10 | 14 | 13 |
| Intake rate (DM g min$^{-1}$ eating) | 2.5 | 2.3 | 3.2 | 3.2 |

6.2.4.2 *Short-term estimates.* Short-term estimates of IR and BM can be made using animals harnessed to prevent the loss of faeces and urine (Erizian, 1932; Allden and Whittaker, 1970; Penning and Hooper, 1985) and weighing them before and after a period of grazing with an allowance for insensible weight loss. Alternatively, by the collection of swallowed herbage from a fistula at the oesophagus (Stobbs, 1973), in both cases in association with the appropriate measurements of GT and bite number. Further details are given in section 6.3.3.

Both of these procedures are dependent on the rapid resumption of grazing activity when the animals are placed on the sample area. Animals should not be fasted before measurements are made because this may increase intake rate and reduce diet selection (Newman *et al.,* 1994b). In addition, groups of animals rather than individuals should be used, as group size has been shown to affect grazing behaviour (Penning *et al.*, 1993, Rind and Phillips, 1999). It has been pointed out (Chapter 7) that individuals in a group should not be used as replicates and, although these two methods apparently give independent estimates of BM and IR, interactions and synchronisation of behaviour amongst animals still occurs and group means should therefore be used.

To overcome the problem of these two methods tending to condition animals to graze, equipment that measures each jaw movement over long periods (see 6.6) and radio controlled valves that allow remote control of extrusa collection from the oesophagus (Raats and Clark, 1992, Raats *et al.*, 1996) can be used.

## 6.3 OBSERVING AND RECORDING GRAZING ACTIVITIES

A detailed knowledge of behaviour patterns derived from direct observation is an essential prerequisite to develop methods and techniques for the collection and analysis of grazing data. Direct observation is laborious and often difficult and indeed, it may be impossible to record manually some parameters e.g continuous detailed monitoring of jaw movements of several animals simultaneously. Observations may have to be carried out in uncomfortable conditions over long periods requiring teams of observers, with a consequent risk in differences between individuals in the interpretation of behavioural activities. These difficulties have provided the impetus to develop automatic recording systems. However, manual observation should always be considered as it has the merit of flexibility and adaptability.

Observations can be facilitated by the use of binoculars and observation posts which can provide some shelter. Raised observation posts are often helpful in maintaining a good field of view and scaffolding towers used by builders, complete with protective covers, can be hired and make good observation posts. Care should be taken to minimise the amount of movement around the plots by the observers to avoid disturbance to the animals as there is evidence that the presence of observers, even at a distance, may influence grazing activity (Jamieson and Hodgson, 1979b). If observation posts are built around the plots then the animals should become accustomed to these before the experimental observations are made.

The majority of grazing activity occurs during the hours of daylight but it is not safe to assume that no grazing will take place during the hours of darkness. The amount of night time grazing will increase with shortening day length and may be different for different herbage species grazed (Penning *et al.*, 1991b). These factors should be taken into account when designing experiments in order to avoid error and bias in the estimation of grazing time. Thus, truly comprehensive observation requires the provision of night viewing facilities. There are many relatively cheap night vision image intensifiers on the market, some fitted with infra-red laser spotlights, and these overcome some of the difficulties of night observations. Shining of flashlights and spotlights onto the animals at night is not recommended, as this often disturbs them and may affect their behaviour patterns.

Many data recording systems are available, ranging from simple data recording forms, Dictaphones, palmtop and laptop computers. The use of data forms provides a structured format for controlling recording sequence and checking errors. Figure 6.3 gives an example of a data form used in an experiment to record behavioural activities of animals grazing contiguous areas of grass and clover. This has been prepared as a computer spread sheet and the data can be input directly into the computer, but a stand by arrangement whereby data can be written by hand onto printed out blank sheets is essential to overcome problems of computer failure. Figure 6.3 shows a simple code developed to record activities and the times at which the animals should be observed, in this case at 5 minute intervals. The data format has been carefully designed so that its automatic analysis can be made by computer. Explanatory comments to amplify standardised recording procedures are also helpful, these can record changes in weather, animal interactions and disturbances to the animals etc.

Where teams of observers are used, it is important to hold preliminary training sessions to ensure that individuals use the same definitions of grazing, idling and ruminating etc. and to deploy observers so as to minimise the risks of confounding observer differences with treatment and time-of-day effects.

Easy identification of the animals is important. In the example given (Figure 6.3) one focal sheep within a group was painted with a colour to make it easily visible. Coloured collars have been used and light reflective numbers fixed to the animals can also help with night observations.

## 6.3.1 Grazing time (GT)

It is possible to make continuous records of the activity of small numbers of animals, but manual recording of GT is usually done on the basis of intermittent records in which animals are observed at intervals and a record made of their activity at the time of observation (section 6.2.1). Recording intervals must be set that give an acceptable accuracy. Rook and Penning (1991) found that the standard deviation of the estimate of grazing time increased with sampling interval (see also Chapter 7). However, their results indicate that the commonly used sampling intervals of 5 or 10 min give acceptable levels of accuracy. In systems where behaviour is monitored at intervals, it is important to try to make an instantaneous decision as to the animals behaviour and 'dwell time' (i.e. the time spent watching an individual animal) should be kept to a minimum. It is difficult to set a maximum dwell time but with experience no more that 5 - 10 s is generally required. Where GT is the sole interest, it will suffice to record 'grazing' or 'not grazing' at each observation. However, it is usual to include observations on ruminating behaviour and whether the animal is standing, walking or lying. Recording this extra information requires little more time.

When observing a group or groups of animals, it is preferable to record activity for each animal individually rather than to categorise the numbers of animals engaged in a particular activity. The former procedure ensures a better base for making statistical comparisons, and for relating behaviour to other variables (e.g. sward state).

The effects of supplements on the dietary preference for grass and clover by sheep

NW23( | Date: 24/7/96 | Observers Name: Claire | Day: Wed

G=Grass   L=Line   C=Clover   S=Standing   L=Lying   E=Eating   R=Ruminating   I=Idling

Figure 6.3. An example of a recording sheet in Microsoft Excel.

HERBAGE INTAKE HANDBOOK

However, this method requires good identification of individual animals. It is important to make observations in a regular sequence to avoid missed or biased records. This is illustrated in Figure 6.3 where a single focal animal, was observed in each group.

Using the procedures outlined above it would be reasonable for a single observer to record 20-30 animals at a time, split into several groups. A set of records of this size could be completed in 5 min, depending on the conditions and complexity of the data to be recorded. On a 10 min cycle this would allow a 5 min break from concentrated observations, or a short period in which to make other observations, of bite rate for example. It is suggested that observers are changed at 4 h intervals.

Manual systems allow records to be made on substantial numbers of animals at one time but, because of the high labour demands, the duration of observations is usually limited to a 24 h period. However, it is advisable to record on at least two days (not necessarily consecutive) in a measurement period.

## 6.3.2. Rate of biting

It is important to decide in advance the basis for defining whether an animal is grazing (6.2) and to pre-determine how jaw movements will be measured, i.e. whether bites will be estimated directly from jaw movements or estimated from head jerks However, a bite is not invariably associated with a head jerk particularly when animals are grazing short swards. In practice, jaw movements will be difficult to observe accurately except at close quarters or with the aid of binoculars, whereas head jerks may be more easily seen.

Records of biting rate are frequently made in association with observations on grazing time and periodicity, in which case the balanced distribution of records throughout the day (section 6.2.2) presents no difficulty. In other cases it is advisable to check the normal pattern of grazing activity in advance. Although bite rates are normally expressed as the number of bites per unit of time (bites min$^{-1}$ or bites sec$^{-1}$) it is normally easier to record manually the time required to take a pre-determined number of bites and then to transform the results. For recording purposes it is useful to have a stop watch with a 'hold' button so that a count can be interrupted if an animal stops grazing temporarily. Whether timing the number of bites taken or counting bites over a given period, it is suggested that a target of 100 to 300 bites should be aimed for, this will require a time period of 1 -3 min. Shorter periods can be used but these tend to overestimate BR e.g. Jamieson and Hodgson (1979a) found that BR measured for 20 uninterrupted bites was on average 16% higher than for BR measured over a 2 min period.

Using the 20-bite technique (recording the time taken for an animal to take 20 bites), measurements of biting rate of at least one per minute can be made during grazing periods. Thus it may be possible to combine measurements of biting rate with more general direct observations of grazing activity, particularly when observations are made at intervals. Using these standard procedures one observer should be able to record biting rates on up to 20 animals, but would require assistance for the recording of grazing activity and biting rate.

### 6.3.3 Rate of intake and intake per bite

Two basic techniques have been used to estimate short-term rates of intake and intake per bite. Erizian (1932) and Allden and Whittaker (1970) fitted animals with apparatus to prevent loss of dung and urine and measured their weight gain over a grazing period. Corrections were made for insensible weight loss. This method was developed further by Penning and Hooper (1985) for use with sheep and Huckle *et al.* (1994) for dairy cows and is described in detail in Chapter 3. Other workers (e.g. Stobbs, 1973) measured the weight of extrusa collected from animals fistulated at the oesophagus which were allowed to graze for periods of up to one hour, but usually for 20 to 30 minutes. In each case records were made of the time which the animals actually spent grazing, and the number of bites taken over this period, using the procedures outlined above.

The weighing technique has now been fairly widely used both for cattle and sheep and obviates the need for surgically prepared animals. Because of ethical considerations, it is becoming increasingly difficult, particularly in the UK, to use surgically prepared animals and legislation restricting their use is in force. The ethics of using surgical prepared animals has been discussed further in Chapter 3.

Procedures for use of animals fistulated at the oesophagus are described in Chapter 3. For estimates of IR and BM it is important to ensure the quantitative recovery of the herbage ingested, and for this purpose it is necessary to use a 'throat plug' placed in the oesophagus just below the fistula. The plug is usually made of plastic foam and should be approx 5-6 cm in length with a diameter of 5 cm for adult cattle, and 3 cm diameter and 3 cm long for adult sheep. Each plug is threaded on a nylon string which is tied around the animals neck to prevent the plug being swallowed. Even using these throat plugs recovery of ingested herbage may not be complete (Table 6.3) and thus BM will be underestimated. It is advisable to carry out checks on recovery of ingested herbage where animals are given a known weight of

*Table 6.3. The recovery of ingested herbage at an oesophageal fistula in animals with and without a throat plug.*

|                       | Mean Recovery | Standard Deviation |
| --------------------- | ------------- | ------------------ |
| Calves[1]             |               |                    |
| Without throat plug   | 0.69          | 0.222              |
| With throat plug      | 0.97          | 0.074              |
|                       |               |                    |
| Adult Sheep[2]        |               | Standard Error     |
| Without throat plug   | 0.41          | 0.045              |
| With throat plug      | 0.84          | 0.045              |

[1] 3 calves x 3 collections (from Jamieson 1975)

[2] 6 sheep x 4 collections (from Valderrabano 1979)

herbage and its recovery at the oesophagus measured. Any animals with consistently low recoveries of herbage can then be rejected. In practice it has been found that many animals with the oesophagus closed with a throat plug are extremely reluctant to graze and excessive salivation make occur. Considerable training may be required before these animals can be used and this must bring into question whether they graze in a similar way to entire animals. To overcome some of these problems Raats and Clarke (1992) have developed radio-controlled valves that can be inserted into the oesophagus which are remotely operated, however, even with this valve the authors report incomplete recovery rates of extrusa (87% SD ± 3.8).

The weighing technique has been used in conjunction with equipment to automatically record number of bites (see below) enabling relatively large numbers of animals to be used. However, where manual observations are used each animal must be watched carefully by an observer and total bites and grazing time recorded. This usually restricts the number of animals that can be used and generally requires relatively small paddocks to ensure that biting activity by the animals can be easily seen and recorded.

### 6.3.4 Movement, searching and walking

Movement i.e. number of steps taken by animals is an essential component in calculating distance travelled and thus energy expenditure by grazing animals. It is difficult to record total number of steps taken in a day unless this is done automatically (see below). However, a sampling routine as described above for grazing, can be adopted. Negi et al. (1993) recorded animal movements to study the energy cost of foraging in diverse pastures whilst Demment and Greenwood (1987) used a portable computer system that facilitated the recording of movement by an observer. To estimate distance travelled by grazing animals the distance per step can be calibrated in separate experiments or by counting the number of steps taken between markers placed at a known distance apart, in the sward being grazed.

The number of bites taken per step can also be estimated and this will give some indication of the intake rate as animals tend to move more on shorter swards where bite mass is low (O'Sullivan, 1984). O'Sullivan (1984) measured the distance walked by beef cattle by tracing their movements on a scaled map.

### 6.4 VIDEO RECORDING

Video recording has now largely replaced the use of filming, as it is relatively cheap and recordings can be studied repeatedly in order to record detailed continuous activity of several behaviours by one person. The technique has been used by Greaves and Wedderburn (1995) to record animal behaviour and to obtained information on animal location.

The authors have used a commercially available CCTV security video system to measure whether animals were grazing on contiguous areas of grass or clover (Parsons et al., 1994b). The system supported the use of up to 16 12V low light cameras simultaneously, and could be programmed to sample each camera in any sequence at variable intervals. The pictures were recorded onto a commercial time-lapse video recorder and could be replayed one camera track at a time or several cameras simultaneously. The disadvantages of this system were that an electricity supply was required in the field and several kilometres of cable were required to link the cameras to the monitoring system. The recordings had to be subsequently analysed manually which was very tedious and time consuming and activities that occurred during the hours of darkness could not be observed. However, image intensifiers are now available that permit observations in almost total darkness and systems have been developed for video analysis (Noldus Information Technology, Wageningen, The Netherlands).

Video recordings should be considered as an extension to manual observations and can provide permanent records of behaviour and useful backup to help interpret any anomalies found in manual observations.

## 6.5 AUTOMATIC RECORDING OF GRAZING BEHAVIOUR

Continuous observation of animals over long periods is laborious, time consuming and often carried out in unpleasant conditions. In addition, some activities such as differentiating between types of jaw movements and their continuous counting are virtually impossible to record manually. These difficulties have lead to the development of many automatic recording systems. It is not possible to list all the systems here but many have been referred to by Penning (1983), Rutter et al. (1997a), Champion et al. (1997) and Laca and WallisDe Fries (2000). The references in these papers form a good basis for investigating the various techniques that have been developed.

There are essentially three phases in automatic recording of grazing behaviour: sensing the activity of interest, transmitting information from the sensor and then recording/processing this information. When developing automatic recording systems it is recommended that all these components should be considered together to develop an integrated system, otherwise large amounts of data may be recorded that cannot be easily summarised and analysed.

Most automatic systems involve mounting sensors on the head of the animal and recording or transmitting equipment on the head or shoulders, using harnesses developed for the purpose. The maximum weight of equipment to be carried should be in the region of 1% to 2% of the bodyweight of the animal but should be kept as light and small as possible to avoid interference with the animal's behaviour. It is essential that any equipment used does not interfere with the recording of the behaviour of interest. Animals should be trained to carry the equipment and 'dummy' sets of equipment can be fitted to the animals and left on for several days for this purpose. Some animals always react adversely to carrying behaviour recording equipment, harnesses or dung bags etc., and their use in experiments should be avoided where possible.

Recording of grazing activity is based on the use of devices to sense movement of either the jaw or head of the animal, usually coupled with an assessment of whether the head and neck of the animal are held below the horizontal (and therefore, presumably, in the grazing position). This approach may allow the recording of both grazing (head down) and ruminating (head up) jaw activity. However, using head position to differentiate between grazing and ruminating can be unreliable in tall swards when animals are grazing on steep slopes or when browsing on trees and shrubs can occur (Penning, 1983). In addition Chacon and Stobbs (1976) showed that up to 20% of jaw movements in cattle, associated with grazing, can occur with the head in the upright position and thus ruminating would be overestimated.

Jaw movements may be sensed and recorded as analogue signals (Figure 6.4). From these analogue signals it can be seen that jaw movements are not only associated

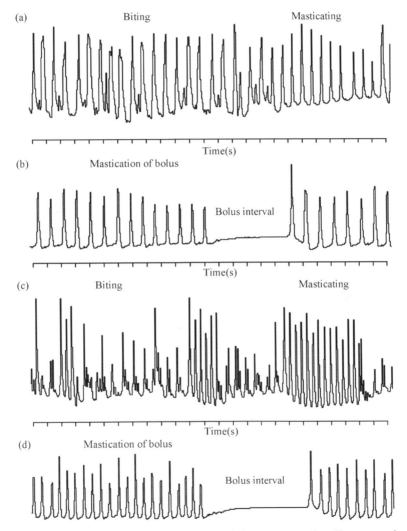

*Figure 6.4. Waveforms recorded by the IGER behaviour recorder (Rutter et al., 1997a) showing jaw movement amplitude (vertical axis, arbitrary scale) plotted against time (horizontal axis, scale 1 sec per division) for (a) grazing in cattle, (b) ruminating in cattle, (c) grazing in sheep and (d) ruminating in sheep.*

with biting but also many non-biting jaw movements occur, these are associated with manipulating and chewing the herbage harvested from the sward. It is also possible to differentiate between ruminating and eating jaw movements from these analogue recordings without the need for a sensor to detect head position. When jaw movements are counted digitally, this information will be lost and unless actual bites can be discriminated from other non-biting jaw movements then biting rate will be overestimated.

In all automatic systems decisions have to be made about the amplitude and frequency of signals which can be accepted as indicative of a particular grazing activity, in relation to the initial settings of the recording devices or in the subsequent analysis of the records. These decisions are essentially those that need to be made in manual recording procedures, though in automatic systems they may be made more objectively and with greater consistency. Whatever the equipment, it is essential to validate it against visual observations, however, this validation may in itself be problematic as modern automatic systems are capable of recording behaviour in far more detail than observers, and disagreements between automatic and manual recording may be due equally to errors in manual observations as in the automatic system (Penning, 1983, Rutter et al., 1997a).

Mechanical and pneumatic recording devices are described briefly in section 6.5.1 and electronic devices in section 6.5.2.

6.5.1. Mechanical and pneumatic devices

The Vibrarecorder (Kienzle Apparate GmbH, Villingen, Germany. UK Agents Kienzle Instruments, 36 Gravelly Industrial Park, Birmingham, B24 8TA) is a vehicle tachograph that was adapted to measure grazing in animals (Allden, 1962) and consists of a pendulum which responds to vibration that produces a trace on pressure sensitive paper. It is driven by a clockwork motor. Because of its weight it had to mounted on the shoulder of sheep but could be mounted on the head, under the chin, or on the neck of cattle. Theoretically it is mounted in such a way that the pendulum is only activated by the grazing movements of the animal. Recording periods ranging from 12 hours to 8 days are available on different models. Some researchers still use vibrarecorders although their use appears to be rapidly declining and the availability of replacement parts etc. is unknown to the authors. They are difficult to keep watertight and are subject to mechanical failure. In addition, they require very careful positioning on the animals and checking for accuracy. Jones and Cowper (1975) found that vibrarecorders over-estimated grazing time by 18.3% compared with visual observations although Jamieson (1975) found a virtual 1: 1 relationship over a series of swards between vibrarecorder estimates and visual observations made at 10 min intervals.

Bêchet (1978) developed the vibrarecorder system further by removing its pendulum and inserting a pneumatic plunger activated by a balloon fitted in the submandibular space of grazing animals. This enabled individual jaw movements to be recorded.

Pneumatic sensors have been used for many years (e.g. Balch, 1958) and more recently have been incorporated into a digital recording system (J-P. Brun, 1990

Personal Communication). They are also used in indoor feeding systems to record jaw movements (see Chapter 5), however, they need careful placement and securing so that changes in air pressure occur due to the jaw movements of the animal.

## 6.5.2 Electrical and electronic devices

Sensors, transducers and electronic systems have been used to measure and record, amongst other things, head position, head movement, jaw movement, lip movement, leg movement and sounds (Canaway et al., 1955, Stobbs and Cowper, 1972, Jones and Cowper, 1975, Leveille et al., 1979, Chambers et al., 1981, Penning, 1983, Brun et al., 1984, Stuth and Searcy, 1987, Luginbuhl et al., 1991, Matsui and Okubo, 1991, 1993, Laca and WallisDeFreis, 2000).

Signals produced by these sensors may be stored on the animals in analogue format (i.e. using tape recorders), digital format, recorded on simple counters carried on the animals or transmitted by radio telemetry. Each of these methods has advantages and disadvantages which the researcher should consider before adopting any particular system. Detailed comparisons of these systems are not possible here, however, digital storage devices fitted to animals now seem to be widely used. These devices have the advantage that they have no moving parts, are small and light, have low power consumption, are relatively cheap and their data can be subsequently analysed by computer.

Leveille et al. (1975) and Brun et al., (1984) were amongst the first workers to develop microcomputer based recording system fitted to animals. The system developed by Brun et al. (1984) used digital recording of the animal's jaw movements and recorded whether there had been any activity in a 2.5s period and, subsequent processing of this data by computer (Prache, 1984), gave time spent eating, ruminating and idling but did not give information on jaw movements. This system has been marketed commercially (J-P Brun, INRA, Theix, France). Rutter et al. (1997a) developed a multi-channel digital recording system based on a microcomputer that could be fitted on a harness to cattle, sheep and goats to record their jaw movements and other parameters such as leg movements (Champion et al., 1997). The recorders may be programmed to have up to a 24 h delayed start after being fitted to the animals, this helps obviate animal behaviour becoming synchronised with the fitting of equipment. Signals from jaw movements are produced using the carbon-filled silicone tube sensor developed by Penning (1983). These are sampled at 20Hz via an analogue to digital converter and may be recorded continuously or at intervals and the data stored on compact flash cards. When sampling is used it is essential that sampling periods are long enough to identify the current activity. These data can be subsequently transferred to a PC and analysed by a computer program (Rutter, 2000). This system is available commercially from: Ultra Sound Advice Ltd., 23 Aberdeen Road, London N5 2UG, UK.

Hybrid systems for recording behaviour and physiological parameters have also been developed that store information continuously on animal mounted recorders which are interrogated at intervals from a remote station. Scheibe et al. (1998) developed such a system (ETHOSYS®) that monitors grazing behaviour using a collar fitted to the animal containing an accelerometer, head position and movement sensor and all the electronics. Data are stored on the animal until it comes within range of a receiving station which automatically downloads and stores the data for subsequent analysis. This system could run for several months before having to be removed from the animals.

For anyone contemplating using automatic behaviour recording systems it is advisable to keep them as simple as possible and to bear in mind that generally the weakest part of the system is the transducer/sensor used. If this is fragile or needs to be kept in a very precise fixed-position on the animal, this will give rise to an unreliable system. When using any electronic system it is essential to ensure that expert help is available for maintenance and trouble shooting.

6.5.2.1 *Position of the head.* This assumes that when an animals is standing with its muzzle close to the ground it is likely to be grazing. Animals may assume this posture without grazing and occasionally graze when lying down so this system is subject to errors. It is also subject to errors where animals are grazing on steep slopes, where clumps of short and tall herbage are grazed in one pasture, or where the animals have access to browse.

A commonly used sensor is a mercury tip-over switch (Jones and Cowper, 1975). A detailed description of such a switch that can be used for this purpose has been given by Champion *et al.* (1997). The switch can be mounted on the head or shoulders of the animals but needs to be carefully adjusted and securely held in position. Alternatively the position of the head can be monitored using a switch activated by an elastic chord running between harnesses on the head and shoulders (Canaway *et al.*, 1955) of the animal. This is a simple device but the tensioning chord is vulnerable to damage. The measurement of head position is usually associated with jaw movement sensors to enable discrimination between grazing and ruminating.

More recently Hansen *et al.* (1992) used a mercury tip switch fitted into a radio-telemetry head collar to monitor the behaviour of wild sheep in Alaska. They hoped to be able to monitor head up/head down to denote whether the animal was feeding but found this was not possible and could only determine whether the animal was active or not.

In practice the authors have found that head position is not a reliable measure of grazing activity.

6.5.2.2 *Jaw movements.* Microswitches that are activated by changes in tension in a cord looped underneath the jaw have been commonly used (Stobbs and Cowper, 1972, Chambers *et al.*, 1981). The adjustment and placement of these switches is critical for reliable recording and they are usually used together with head position to differentiate between grazing and ruminating jaw movements.

Various other devices have been used including electrodes placed over or implanted in the *masseter* muscle to monitor the electromyogram (Nichols, 1966); reed switches to measure the wrinkling in the skin above the nose as a bite is taken (Stuth and Searcy, 1987) and more commonly balloons placed in the submandibular space to give changes in air pressure when the jaws are opened (Balch, 1958, Bêchet, 1978, J-P. Brun, 1990, personal communication).

One of the most commonly used sensors is a silicone rubber tube filled with graphite (Penning, 1983). This is formed into a noseband so that when the animal moves it jaws the noseband is stretched and its electrical resistance increases. This increase in resistance is sensed by an electronic circuit and the signal recorded. The positioning of the noseband on the animal is not critical as the signal produced is 'A/C coupled' i.e. the circuit used discriminates against low frequency (<1Hz) changes such as those produced by the sensor slowly changing its position on the animal and gives a constant base line. The signals produced may be recorded continuously in analogue or digital form (Penning, 1983, Rutter *et al.*, 1997a) and this obviates the need for a sensor to measure head position as it is relatively easy to discriminate between the different wave forms produced by grazing and ruminating jaw movements (Figure 6.4). Figure 6.4. also shows that during grazing jaw movements other than those associated with biting occur. A detailed interpretation of these waveforms is given by Gibb (1996). The ratio of biting to non-biting jaw movements may change with changes in sward state and time of day for cattle and sheep (Penning *et al.*, 1991a, Gibb *et al.*, 1999 and Orr *et al.*, 1997). Thus, simply counting grazing jaw movements and not discriminating between biting and non-biting will overestimate the number of bites and, if these counts are used in the calculation of bite mass, this will lead to it being underestimated.

Sounds made by jaw movements of grazing animals have been recorded and transmitted by a radio microphone fitted to the head of the animal and these sounds have been used to count bites (Laca and WallisDeVries, 2000). This technique is still undergoing development and as yet the automatic analysis of the sounds produced has not been fully developed. From the sounds produced during grazing, it is possible to discriminate between bites and non-biting jaw movements. This technique shows great promise and is undergoing further development.

6.5.2.3 *Head Movements.* Although head movements have been used as a routine indicator of grazing in manual studies and provide the basis of Vibrarecorder records, they have not generally been used in electronic recording systems. Chambers *et al.* (1981) used accelerometers fitted to the heads of grazing animals to measure the head jerks associated with biting. This system has the advantage that it can discriminate between biting and non-biting jaw movements and is not confounded by jaw movements associated with ruminating. Penning (1983) tested accelerometers but found that interference from head movements etc. made it difficult to interpret the signals from jaw movements. In order to reduce interference caused by movements other than jaw movements, it is necessary to filter the signal produced and unless these filters are carefully calibrated data may be lost.

6.5.2.4 *Walking, standing lying and location.* A knowledge of walking, standing and lying is essential for developing energy budgets for grazing animals. Several workers have used pedometers to measure walking (Powell, 1968, Walker *et al.*, 1985, Coulter and O'Sullivan (1988). Pedometers usually consist of a pendulum that swings when the animal walks and each swing of the pendulum activates a counter allowing total steps to be recorded. One disadvantage of this system is that pedometers have to be calibrated for individual animals.

O'Neill *et al.,* (1987) used an infra red proximity switch fitted on one leg and a reflector on the other to count steps taken by draught animals. This system was later modified by Howell and Paice (1988) who replaced the infra red switch with an accelerometer attached to the lower part of the leg.

Stuth and Searcy (1987) used a magnetically operated reed switch mounted on a length of elastic that hung loosely by the animal's side when the leg was vertical. When the leg moved forward the elastic was stretched allowing the magnet to move away from the reed switch causing an electrical contact to be made, signifying a step.

To measure standing and lying Canaway *et al.* (1955) used a microswitch as a pressure sensor to record when an animal was lying, an alternative system using a pressure sensor was developed by Dohi *et al.* (1993). Brun (1994, personal communication) developed a lying/standing sensor based on a mercury switch hanging below the animal (dangler switch). This was further developed and has been fully described by Champion *et al.* (1997). Champion *et al.* (1997) then fitted this type of mercury switch to the legs of animals and found that it could not only measure walking, but also standing and lying. The output from this switch was input into one of the recording channels of the digital recorder described by Rutter *et al.* (1997a). The signal was sampled at 20 Hz and stored on the recorder on the animal. Subsequently the signal was analysed by a computer program that used software filtering to remove signal noise and interpreted whether animals were standing or lying and recorded each step taken. The accuracy of detection of lying, standing and walking measured automatically was not significantly different from manual observations.

Recently, (R.A. Champion, personal communication 2002) adapted commercially available equipment (TI-RFid S2000,Texas Instruments, Radio Frequency Identification Systems, Plano, Texas 75023,USA) that identifies individual animals from transponders, fitted either as an ear tag (Allflex Europe (UK) Ltd., Unit 7, Galaway Business Park, Hawick, TD9 8PZ) or as bolus in the rumen (Shearwell Data Ltd., Putham Farm, Wheddon Cross, Minehead, Somerset, TA24 7AS, UK) to measure when animals pass fixed points when grazing. This technique was designed to measure whether animals were grazing on large patches of clover or grass.

The wider scale movement and position of free-ranging animals has been monitored using a differential Global Position System (GPS) (Rutter *et al.* 1997b). GPS receivers were mounted on sheep and their output was stored on a digital recorder. After several days the sheep were rounded up and their recorders removed. It was possible from the data to monitor the movements of the sheep over their range. Hulbert *et al. (*1998a, 1998b) reported using lightweight GPS receivers and radio transmitters incorporated into collars fitted to sheep. The GPS data were transmitted and stored on a computer and position of the animal and its movements plotted. The accuracy of positioning by the system was better than 10m. GPS receivers are being made smaller and are becoming cheaper and will obviously be useful in future studies of free ranging herbivores and their use of different plant communities and habitats.

## 6.6 CONCLUSIONS

It has not been possible here to cover this subject in great depth because of the many advances in electronics and computing which have given rise to the rapid development of many techniques to record grazing behaviour. Over the last 10 to 15 years, our understanding of the grazing process and the relationship between ingestive behaviour of animals and sward state, has been greatly advanced by using automated techniques to monitor animal behaviour. However, before adopting any technique the researcher should investigate the available methods thoroughly, preferably with the help of an experienced adviser. Some preliminary manual observations can give vital pointers to the type of behaviour that is occurring and how relevant this is to understanding experimental results, this in turn will give indications of whether these parameters can be monitored automatically and the type of equipment needed to record them. Care should be taken that any equipment fitted to the animal does not interfere with its behaviour and animals should generally be trained to become accustomed to wearing harnesses and carrying equipment before experimental measurements are made. It is hoped that this chapter will provide a useful starting point for the investigation of appropriate methods and techniques in grazing behaviour studies.

## 6.7 REFERENCES

ALLDEN W.G. (1962) Rate of herbage intake and grazing time in relation to herbage availability. *Proceedings of the Australian Society of Animal Production,* **4**, 163-166.

ALLDEN W.G. AND WHITTAKER, I. A. McD (1970) The determination of herbage intake by grazing sheep: the interrelationship of factors of factors influencing herbage intake and availability. *Australian Journal of Agricultural Research,* **21**, 755-766.

BALCH C.C. (1958) Observations on the act of eating in cattle. *British Journal of Nutrition,* **12**, 330-345.

BÊCHET G. (1978) Enregistrement des activités alimentaires et meryciques des ovins au pâturage. *Annales de Zootechnie,* **27**, 107-113.

BRUN J-P., PRACHE S. AND BÊCHET G. (1984) A portable device for use in eating behaviour studies. *Proceedings of the 5th European Grazing Workshop, Edinburg, UK.*

CANNAWAY R.J., RAYMOND W.F. AND TAYLER J.C. (1955) The automatic recording of animal behaviour in the field. *Electronic Engineering, March,* pp. 102-105.

CHACON E. AND STOBBS T.H. (1976) Estimation of herbage consumption by grazing cattle using measurements of easting behaviour. *Journal of the British Grassland Society,* **31**, 81-87.

CHAMBERS A.R.M., HODGSON J. AND MILE J.A. (1981) The development and use of equipment for the automatic recording of ingestive behaviour in sheep and cattle. *Grass and Forage Science,* **36**, 97-105.

CHAMPION R.A., RUTTER S.M. AND PENNING P.D. (1997) An automatic system to monitor lying, standing and walking behaviour of grazing animals. *Applied Animal Behaviour Science,* **54**, 291-305.

CHAMPION R.A., RUTTER, S.M., PENNING, P.D. AND ROOK, A.J. (1994) Temporal variation in grazing behaviour of sheep and the reliability of sampling periods. *Applied Animal Behaviour Science,* **42**, 99-108.

COULTER B.S. AND O'SULLIVAN M. (1988) A remote monitor for animal behaviour using radio telemetry. *Proceedings of the 12th General Meeting of the European Grassland Federation, Dublin, Ireland, July 4-7,* pp.450-454.

DEMMENT M.W. AND GREENWOOD G.B. (1987) The use of a portable computer for real time monitoring of grazing behaviour in the field. *Journal of Range Management,* **40,** 284-285.

DOHI H., YAMADA A., TSUDA S., SUMIKAWA T. AND ENTSU S. (1993) A pressure-sensitive sensor for measuring the characteristics of standing mounts of cattle. *Journal of Animal Science,* **71,** 369-372.

ERIZIAN C. (1932) Eine neue Methode zur Bestimmung der vom Vieh gefressenen Menge Weidefutters. *Zeitschrift für Tierzüchtung und Züchtungsbiologie. Rheihe B.,* **25,** 443-459.

FORBES J.M., JACKSON D.A., JOHNSON C.L., STOCKILL P. AND HOYLE B.S. (1986) A method for the monitoring of food intake and feeding behaviour of individual cattle kept in a group. *Research and Development in Agriculture,* **3,** 175-180.

GIBB M.J. (1996) Animal grazing/intake terminology definitions. In: M.G. Keane and E.G. O'Riordan (eds). Potential for and Consequences of Extensification of Beef and Sheep Production on the Grasslands of the EC. Occasional Publication No.3. *Proceedings of a Workshop held in Dublin on September 24-25, 1996 for Concerted Action AIR3-CT93-0947* pp. 21-37.

GIBB M.J., HUCKLE C.A. AND NUTHALL. R. (1998) Effect of time of day on grazing behaviour by lactating dairy cows. *Grass and Forage Science,* **53,** 41-46.

GIBB M.J., HUCKLE C.A., NUTHALL. R. AND ROOK A.J. (1999) The effect of physiological state (lactating or dry) and sward surface height on grazing behaviour and intake by dairy cows. *Applied Animal Behaviour Science,* **63,** 269-287.

GORDON I.J. (1995) Animal-based techniques for grazing ecology research. *Small Ruminant Research,* **16,** 203-214.

GREAVES L.A. AND WEDDERBURN M.E. (1995) Comparisons of the behaviour of goats and sheep on an eroded hill pasture. *Applied Animal Behaviour Science,* **42,** 207-216.

HANSEN M.C., GARNER G.W. AND FANCY S.G. (1992) Comparison of 3 methods for evaluating activity of Dall's sheep. *Journal of Wildlife Management,* **56,** 661-668.

HOWELL P.J.L. AND PAICE M.E.R. (1988) An adaptive data logging system for animal power studies. *Agricultural Engineering 88. International Conference on Agricultural Engineering International Conference, Paris, March 2-5.* 7 pp.

HUCKLE C.A., NUTHALL R. AND GIBB M.J. (1994) The use of short-term weight changes to measure intake rates in grazing dairy cattle. *Fourth BGS Research Conference, British Grassland Society, September 1994,* pp. 157-158.

HULBERT I.A.R., FRENCH J., GOODING R.F., RACKHAM D., HOLLAND J.P. AND WATERHOUSE A. (1998a) A test of the accuracy of the differential Global Positioning System (DGPS) to track free-ranging hill sheep. *Proceedings of the IXth European Intake Workshop, Institute of Grassland and Environmental Research, November,* pp. 27-30.

HULBERT I.A.R., WYLLIE J.T.B., WATERHOUSE A., FRENCH J. AND McNULTY D. (1998b) A note on the circadian rhythm and feeding activity of sheep fitted with a lightweight GPS collar. *Appiled Animal Behaviour Science,* **60,** 359-364.

JAMIESON W.S. (1975) Studies on the intake and grazing behaviour of cattle and sheep. *Ph.D. Thesis, University of Reading.* pp. 187.

JAMIESON W.S. AND HODGSON J. (1979a) The effect of daily herbage allowance and sward characteristics upon the ingestive behaviour of calves under strip-grazing management. *Grass and Forage Science,* **34,** 261-271.

JAMIESON W.S. AND HODGSON J. (1979b) The effects of variation in sward characteristics upon the ingestive behaviour and herbage intake of calves and lambs under a continuous stocking management. *Grassand Forage Science*, **34**, 273-282.

JONES R.J. AND COWPER L.J. (1975) A lightweight electronic device for measurement of grazing time of cattle. *Tropical Grasslands*, **9**, 235-241.

LACA E.A. AND WALLISDEVRIES M.F. (2000) Acoustic measurement of intake and grazing behaviour of cattle. *Grass and Forage Science*, **55**, 97-104.

LEVEILLE M., JOUNAY J.P. AND BRUN J-P (1979) Analyse automatique du compartement alimentaire et merycique chez le mouton. *Annales de Biologie Animale Biochemie, Biophysique*, **19**, 889-893.

LUGINBUHL J-M., POND K.R., BURNS J.C., FISHER D.S. AND RUSS J.C. (1991) A computer interface system to monitor the ingestive behaviour of grazing ruminants. *Proceedings of the 2$^{nd}$ Grazing Livestock Nutrition Conference, 2-3 August, Steamboat Springs, Colorado*, pp. 177.

LYNCH J.J. HINCH, G.N. AND ADAMS, D.B. (1992) The behaviour of sheep. *Published C.A.B. International UK and CSIRO Australia. pp.* 237.

MATSUI K., AND OKUBO T. (1991) A method for quantification of jaw movements suitable for use on free-ranging cattle. *Applied Animal Behaviour Science*, **32**, 107-116.

MATSUI K., AND OKUBO T. (1993) A new ambulatory data-logging system for a long-term determination of grazing and ruminating behaviour on free-ranging cattle. *Proceedings of the XVII International Grassland Congress, Palmerston North, New Zealand, 2-21 February.*

METZ J.H.M. (1975) Time patterns of feeding and rumination in domestic cattle. *Wageningen: Communications Agricultural University*, 75-120.

NEGI G.C.S., RIKHARI H.C., RAM J. AND SINGH S.P. (1993) Foraging niche characteristics of horses, sheep and goats in alpine meadows of the Indian Central Himalaya. *Journal of Applied Ecology*, **30**, 383-394.

NEWMAN J.A., PARSONS, A.J. AND PENNING, P.D. (1994a) A note on the behavioural strategies used by grazing animals to alter their intake rates. *Grass and Forage Science*, **49**, 502-505.

NEWMAN J.A., PARSONS A.J., THORNLEY J.H.M., PENNING P.D. AND KREBS J.R. (1995) Optimal diet selection by a generalist grazing herbivore. *Functional Ecology*, **9**, 255-268.

NEWMAN J.A., PENNING P.D., PARSONS A.J., HARVEY A. AND ORR R.J. (1994b) Fasting affects intake behaviour and diet preference of grazing sheep. *Animal Behaviour*, **47**, 185-193.

NICHOLS G. DE LA M. (1966) Radio transmission of sheep's jaw movements. *New Zealand Journal of Agricultural Research*, **9**, 468-473.

O'NEIL D. H., HOWELL P.J.L , PAICE M.E.R. AND KEMP D.C. (1987) An instrumentation system to measure the performance of draught animals at work. *Paper presented to 'National Seminar on Animal Energy Utilisation', Central Institute of Agricultural Engineering, Bhopal, India, 24-25 January.* 10 pp.

O'SULLIVAN M. (1984) Measurement of grazing behaviour and herbage intake on two different grazing management systems for beef production. *Grassland Beef Production*, Dordrecht, Netherthlands, Martinus Nijhoff, pp. 141-150.

ORR R.J., PENNING P.D., HARVEY A. AND CHAMPION R.A. (1997) Diurnal patterns of intake rate by sheep grazing monocultures of ryegrass or white clover. *Applied Animal Behaviour Science*, **52**, 65-77.

PARSONS A.J. NEWMAN J.A. PENNING P.D. HARVEY A. AND ORR R.J. (1994b) Diet preference of sheep: effects of recent diet, physiological state and species abundance. *Journal of Animal Ecology*, **63**, 465-478.

PARSONS A.J., THORNLEY, J.H.M., NEWMAN, J.A. AND PENNING, P.D. (1994a) A mechanistic model of some physical determinants of intake rate and diet selection in a two-species temperate grassland sward. *Functional Ecology,* **8**, 187-204.

PENNING P.D. (1983) A technique to record automatically some aspects of grazing and ruminating behaviour in sheep. *Grass and Forage Science,* **38**, 89-96.

PENNING P.D. (1986) Some effects of sward conditions on grazing behaviour and intake by sheep. In: O. Gudmundsson (ed). *Grazing research at northern latitudes. Plenum Publishing Corporation.* pp 219-226.

PENNING P.D. AND HOOPER G.E. (1985) An evaluation and use of short-term weight changes in grazing sheep for estimating herbage intake. *Grass and Forage Science,* **40**, 79-84.

PENNING P.D., PARSONS, A.J., HOOPER, G.E. AND ORR, R.J (1994) Intake behaviour responses by sheep to changes in sward characteristics under rotational grazing. *Grass and Forage Science,* **49**, 476-486.

PENNING P.D., PARSONS A.J., NEWMAN A.J., ORR R.J. AND HARVEY A. (1993) The effects of group size in grazing time in sheep. *Applied Animal Behaviour Science,* **37**, 101-109.

PENNING P.D., PARSONS, A.J., ORR, R.J., HARVEY, A. AND CHAMPION R.A. (1995) Intake and behaviour responses by sheep, in different physiological states, when grazing monocultures of grass or white clover. *Applied Animal Behaviour Science,* **45**, 63-78.

PENNING P.D., PARSONS, A.J., ORR, R.J. AND TREACHER, T.T. (1991a) Intake behaviour responses by sheep to changes in sward characteristics under continuous stocking. *Grass and Forage Science,* **46**, 15-28.

PENNING P.D., STEEL G.L. AND JOHNSON R.J. (1984) Further development and use of an automatic recording system in sheep grazing studies. *Grass and Forage Science,* **39**, 345-351.

PENNING P.D., ROOK, A.J. AND ORR R.J. (1991b) Patterns of ingestive behaviour of sheep continuously stocked on monocultures of ryegrass or white clover. *Applied Animal Behaviour Science,* **31**, 237-250.

PHILLIPS C.J.C. (1993) Cattle Behaviour. *Published Farming Press Books. Ipswich, UK. pp.* 212.

POWELL T.L. (1968) Pedometer measurements of the distance walked by grazing sheep in relation to weather. *Journal of the British Grassland Society,* **23**, 98-102.

PRACHE S. (1984) Electronic device to determine influence of number of lambs suckled and feed supplementation on grazing behaviour. *Proceedings of the 5th European Grazing Workshop, Endinburgh,UK.*

RAATS J.G. AND CLARK B.K. (1992) Remote control of oesophageal fistula samples in goats. *Small Ruminant Research,* **7**, 245-251.

RAATS J.G., WEBBER L., TAINTON N.M. AND PEPE D. (1996) An evaluation of the equipment for oesophageal fistula valve technique. *Small Ruminant Research,* **21**, 213-216.

RIND M.I. AND PHILLIPS C.J. (1999) The effect of group size on the ingestive and social behaviour of grazing dairy cows. *Animal Science,* **68**, 589-596.

ROOK A.J. AND PENNING P.D. (1991) Stochastic models of grazing behaviour in sheep. *Applied Animal Behaviour Science,* **32**, 167-177.

RUCKEBUSCH Y. (1975) The hypnogram as an index of adaptation of farm animals to changes in their environment. *Applied Animal Ethology,* **2**, 3-18.

RUTTER S.M. (2000) Graze: A program to analyze recordings of the jaw movements of ruminants. *Behaviour Research Methods, Instruments and Computers,* **32**, 86-92.

RUTTER S.M. (2002) Behaviour of sheep and goats. In: Jensen P. (ed.) *1. Livestock Behaviour. 2. Domestic Animals' Behaviour. CABI Publishing, Wallingford and New York.* pp. 145-148.

RUTTER S.M., BERESFORD N.A. AND ROBERTS G. (1997b) Use of GPS to identify grazing areas of hill sheep. *Computers and Electronics in Agriculture,* **17**, 177-188.

RUTTER S.M., CHAMPION R.A. AND PENNING P.D. (1997a) An automatic system to record foraging behaviour in free-ranging ruminants. *Applied Animal Behaviour Science,* **54**, 185-195.

SCHEIBE K.M., SCHLEUSNER Th., BERGER A., EICHHORN K., LANGBEIN J., DAL ZOTTO L. AND STREICH W.J. (1998) ETHOSYS® - new system for recording and analysis of behaviour of free-ranging domestic animals and wild life. *Applied Animal Behaviour Science,* **55,** 195-211.

SIBLEY R.M., NOTT H.R.M. AND FLETCHER D.J. (1990) Splitting behaviour into bouts. *Animal Behaviour,* **39**, 63-69.

SPALINGER D.E. AND HOBBS N.T. (1992) Mechanisms of foraging in mammalian herbivores: new models of functional responses. *American Naturalist,* **140**, 325-348.

STOBBS T.H. (1973) The effect of plant structure on the intake of tropical pastures. I. Variation in the bite size of grazing cattle. *Australian Journal of Agricultural Research,* **24**, 809-819.

STOBBS T.H. AND COWPER L.J. (1972) Automatic measurement of the jaw movements of dairy cows during grazing and rumination. *Tropical Grasslands,* **6**, 67-69.

STUTH J. AND SEARCY S. (1987) A new electronic approach to monitoring ingestive behaviour of cattle. *Herbivore Nutrition Research. Second International Symposium on the Nutrition of Herbivores, University of Queensland, Brisbane, Australia, 6-10 July. Occasional Pulication Australian Society of Animal Production,* 236 pp.

TOLLKAMP B.J., ALLCROFT D.J., AUSTIN E.J., NIELSEN B.L. AND KYRIAZAKIS I. (1998) Satiety splits feeding behaviour into bouts. *Journal of Theoretical Biology,* **194**, 235-250.

VALDERRABANO J. (1979) Techniques of measuring intake in grazing sheep. *M.Phil. Thesis, University of Reading 1979,* 145 pp.

WALKER J.W., HEITSCHMIDT R.K. AND DOWHOWER S.L. (1985) Evaluation of pedometers for measuring distance travelled by cattle on two grazing systems. *Journal of Range Management,* **38**, 90-93.

CHAPTER 7

# STATISTICAL CONSIDERATIONS IN THE DESIGN OF HERBAGE INTAKE STUDIES

A. J. Rook

7.1    Introduction
7.2    Dependence between animals grazing in groups
7.2.1    Arguments for and against using group or individual animal as replicates
7.3    Dependence of observations on the same unit over time
7.4    Sources of variation
7.5    Conclusions

## 7.1 INTRODUCTION

The design of herbage intake studies, like any other experiment, must take into consideration basic statistical principles, such as replication and randomisation. These are considered in great detail in standard statistical texts (e.g. Cochran and Cox, 1964), with applications to field experimentation covered by, for example, Pearce (1983) and Pearce *et al.* (1988). Some specific concerns relating to pasture experiments are considered by Thomas and Laidlaw (1993) in the companion volume to this book. In this chapter attention will be focused on the particular design problems which arise when grazing animals are used in experiments. These may conveniently be considered under three headings, (a) the dependence between animals within groups, (b) the dependence of observations on the same animals over time and (c) the relative importance of different sources of error.

## 7.2 DEPENDENCE BETWEEN ANIMALS GRAZING IN GROUPS

Most experimenters accept the need to replicate plots or paddocks when the effects of different treatments on sward characteristics are to be compared. However, when the chief interest is in animal characteristics, such as herbage intake, animals within a paddock are often treated as replicates. There is an implicit assumption in designs of this type that each animal's grazing behaviour, and hence herbage intake, is independent of the behaviour and intake of its companions in the same paddock. In this section evidence which casts doubt on this assumption is reviewed and the implications for experimental design are discussed.

It has recently been shown that the grazing behaviour of both sheep (Rook and Penning, 1991) and dairy cows (Rook and Huckle, 1995) kept in groups is highly synchronised. An example showing the activity pattern of a group of seven ewes grazing a perennial ryegrass sward is given in Figure 7.1. The synchrony of eating can be seen clearly, with the large synchronized meal immediately before sunset being particularly evident. Rook and Penning (1991) developed a method, based on a kappa coefficient of agreement (Siegel and Castellan, 1988), for comparing observed synchrony with that expected if animals were acting independently. Both for sheep (Rook and Penning, 1991) and cows (Rook and Huckle, 1995) synchrony was found to be significantly greater than that expected due to chance. This lack of independence between animals in a group shows that they cannot be regarded as replicates in the design and analysis of experiments.

This consideration remains important when the sward is simply a background treatment and experimental interest centres on the effect of non-sward characteristics, for example the amount of supplement offered. Benham (1984) looked at the effect of cows with an intrinsically high grazing time on those with a low grazing time in an unsupplemented continuously stocked system. He found no facilitatory effect on grazing time but did find that the animals with low grazing times did not in general lie down while their companions were grazing. Benham (1984) was unable to demonstrate conclusively that social facilitation occurred between supplemented and unsupplemented animals grazing together in a rotational grazing system. However, he pointed out that this experiment was compromised in a number of ways and cannot be regarded as conclusive. It would therefore be unwise to split animals grazing a paddock into groups each receiving different amounts of supplement as the possibility remains that one group may facilitate increased or decreased grazing by another. Each distinct treatment group should always graze exclusively on a paddock.

In some circumstances the use of separate paddocks for groups receiving different non-sward treatments could lead to undesirable differences between the swards in the different paddocks which are confounded with the direct effects of the treatment. This may be avoided by rotating different treatment groups between paddocks on a daily basis. An example of this type of design was used by Rook, Huckle and Wilkins (1994). When more than two treatments are used it is important that systematic effects due to treatment order on a paddock are avoided. This may be achieved by adaptation of standard experimental designs for balanced residual effects, as given for example by Cochran and Cox (1950). An example based on a 4 x 4 latin square is shown in Table 7.1.

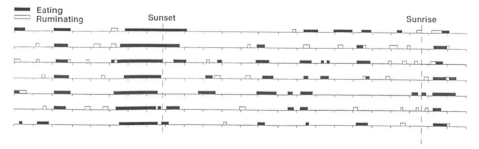

*Figure 7.1. Individual activity patterns of seven ewes, grazing in a group on a perennial ryegrass sward in October.*

*Table 7.1. A design balanced for residual effects.*

| day | paddock 1 | paddock 2 | paddock 3 | paddock 4 |
|-----|-----------|-----------|-----------|-----------|
| 1 | A | B | C | D |
| 2 | B | C | D | A |
| 3 | D | A | B | C |
| 4 | C | D | A | B |
| 5 | C | D | A | B |
| 6 | D | A | B | C |
| 7 | B | C | D | A |
| 8 | A | B | C | D |
| 9 | A | B | C | D |

Sometimes it will be necessary to obtain measurements on an individual animal rather than on the mean of a group. Alternatively it may be impossible to measure all animals in the group with the resources available. These situations may be addressed by using a focal animal within a group. This approach avoids the problems with using individually penned animals outlined below.

In indoor feeding experiments animals are usually housed individually or kept in groups but fed individually using Calan-Broadbent doors. It is generally assumed that this overcomes the problem of non-independence observed at pasture as animals do not need to compete for food. However, Metz and Mekking (1978) found that the start and end of meals were both more synchronized when pairs of cows kept indoors were in adjacent pens than when they were kept apart. A re-examination of the design of indoor experiments is therefore also required.

The area of land available for experimentation is usually a fixed resource. Therefore, if experiments using animals as replicates are redesigned to include replication of paddocks, it follows that the number of animals in each group will be smaller unless the number of treatments is reduced. However, reducing the number of animals in a group brings it own pitfalls. Penning *et al.* (1993) have shown that grazing time of ewes is significantly decreased when group size falls below 4 (Figure 7.2) and Rind and Phillips (1999) have shown that groups of four cows during grazing are more vigilant than groups of eight or 16 cows. It would thus be unwise to design experiments using groups of less than 4 animals. These results also cast doubt on the applicability of results obtained in experiments in which isolated individuals are used to graze turves or artificial swards. The use of sufficient replicate groups of sufficient size will sometimes limit the number of treatments which can be accommodated within the available area. However, if the treatments are levels of a quantitative factor it is not necessary to replicate at each level, instead a regression design may be employed. This has been strongly recommended by Bransby (1989) as a desirable method in its own right in the context of different grazing levels (stocking rate, sward surface height etc.).

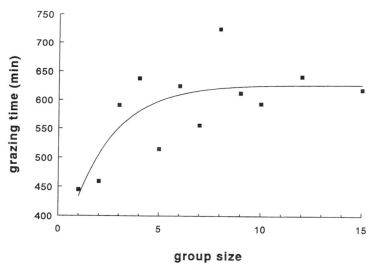

*Figure 7.2. Grazing time of sheep (min 24 h⁻¹) as a function of group size. Points are mean values for three ewes (Penning et al.,1993).*

In some circumstances the opportunity to replicate groups may be severely restricted and individual animals may have to be used to obtain sufficient degrees of freedom. In this case the dependence between observations on individual animals can be reduced , although not eliminated, by observing different animals on different days. An example of this type of design was used by Newman *et al.* (1989).

7.2.1 *Arguments for and against using groups or individual animals as replicates.* The conclusion of Rook and Huckle (1995) that individual cows should not be used as replicates in grazing experiments because of lack of independence between animals within a group has been criticised by Phillips (1998). He argued that synchronisation of behaviour and allelomimicry do not necessarily imply that the behaviour of individual animals is interdependent. Phillips suggested that for some behaviours the use of individuals as replicates may be justifiable. Rook (1999) argued against this approach and pointed out that social facilitation is not the only factor causing dependence in grazing studies and that competition for food is also of great importance; what one animal has eaten another cannot.

Weary and Fraser (1998) commented that the requirement for independence between observations applies to all statistical tests and not just to ANOVA and that the approach by Phillips (1998) is unusual, in that he tries to provide a rationale for ignoring the problem of pseudo-replication within certain constraints. Weary and Fraser (1998) give examples of circumstances when individual animals may be used as replicates but conclude that using individuals as 'replicates' when treatments are applied to herds is an instance of pseudo-replication and in such cases the data from individuals cannot be used as replicates in statistical tests of treatment effects.

Iason and Elston (2002) proposed a possible way forward by investigating the correlations between individuals within groups, and correlations between variables within individuals, and the resultant statistical effects of these correlations. They suggest (and this view is supported by Phillips, 2002) that philosophical refusal to contemplate testing treatment effects against variation between individuals is premature and may give rise to a high rate of Type II statistical errors. However, correlations between animals within a group cannot be ignored, and conclusions drawn and analyses carried out only at the level of the individual or only at the level of the group, may be invalid (Knowles and Green, 2002). Knowles and Green (2002) recommend the use of hierarchical or 'multi-level' models to analyse this type of data. Multilevel models have been recognised in areas of biological, medical and human research for some years (Knowles and Green, 2002) and an introductory book by Goldstein (1995) has been published on the subject. Additional information and support for the MLwiN program is available on the Institute of Education Site, London, (http://multilevel.ioe.ac.uk/index.html).

This debate has brought to light the requirement for further work to clarify some of the issues raised and the urgent need for further development of methods for the statistical analysis for this type of data. Pending such development, the conservative approach of only analysing grouped data advocated by Rook (1999) is to be preferred.

## 7.3 DEPENDENCE OF OBSERVATIONS ON THE SAME UNIT OVER TIME.

Herbage intake studies often involve the use of repeated measurements on the same replicates over time. The errors associated with measurements at each time point are not usually independent and thus violate the assumptions of standard statistical analyses. These problems may be overcome by adopting methods designed specifically for the analysis of repeated measurements. One of the most commonly used methods is the fitting of summary statistics over time (Rowell and Walters, 1976). These summary statistics range from a simple mean across time for each experimental unit to the parameters of non-linear functions of time. There are a number of other approaches to repeated measures data which are discussed, for example, by Kenward (1987).

Dependence between successive observations is also important in designing grazing behaviour studies where observations are made at discrete time intervals and the behaviour observed at any time point is regarded as being representative of that which has occurred since the previous observation. Such sampling schemes have often been based on a multinomial model of behaviour in which the activity of the animal at a particular time is regarded as being independent of its activity at all previous times. However, in reality different activities occur in well defined bouts and not at random over the day as assumed by this model (Figure 7.1). Smith and Hodgson (1984) investigated the performance of a binomial sampling model and suggested that it overestimated the error in estimating the true grazing time. They did not consider any alternative models. Rook and Penning (1991) carried out a similar exercise and having pointed out some flaws in the method of Smith and Hodgson (1984) concluded that the errors were in fact underestimated rather than overestimated using the multinomial model. Rook and Penning (1991) also considered two alternative models which take account of the bout structure in such data, the Markov process and the age dependent process. In a Markov process the probability of an activity occurring in any time period is dependent only on the activity occurring in the immediately preceding period. In an age dependent model the probability is dependent not only on the activity in the preceding period but on how long that activity has continued. This is more realistic biologically. However, Rook and Penning (1991) found that the Markov process adequately represented the grazing behaviour of sheep and is more mathematically tractable. They also showed that the Markov model was more realistic than the multinomial model for representing the errors associated with discontinuous recording and recommended that sampling schemes should be designed using this model.

## 7.4 SOURCES OF VARIATION

In designing grazing experiments trade-offs are often required between the number of replicates measured at one time and the number of times each replicate is measured. These decisions will depend on the relative magnitude of between group and between day variation. It has been shown (Champion *et al.* 1994) that the basic daily pattern of grazing activity of sheep is repeatable and that the nycterohemeral grazing pattern over 24 h may be taken as representative of that over a period of at least 8 days. This suggests that repeated observation may not be very useful. The pattern does however vary within a 24-h period and experiments using short term measurement of intake must take this into account. Although the basic pattern was highly repeatable, the repeatability of grazing time within each hour of the day for individual animals was low. However, Phillips and Denne (1988) found that between cow variation in grazing time was greater than between day variation. It is thus necessary to evaluate the relative importance of these factors in each experimental situation where animal and environmental factors are different and to distribute the allocation of resources accordingly.

## 7.5 CONCLUSIONS

In conclusion the following recommendations should be followed when designing herbage intake studies.
a.  Paddocks should be replicated even when the prime interest is in animal characteristics.
b.  Group sizes should not be too small.
c.  Animals receiving different non-sward treatments should graze separate paddocks with rotation of paddocks to obtain similar sward conditions across treatments if required.
d.  Sampling schemes for discrete observations over time should be based on a Markov model.
e.  Compromise solutions such as the use of regression designs are sometimes required.
f.  The relative magnitude of different sources of variation should be considered.

## 7.6 REFERENCES

BENHAM P. F. J. (1984) Social organization in groups of cattle and the interrelationships between social and grazing behaviours under different management systems. *Ph.D. Thesis, University of Reading.*

BRANSBY D. I. (1989) Compromises in the design and conduct of grazing experiments. *Grazing Research: Design, Methodology and Analysis, Crop Science Society of America, Special Publication,* **16**, 53-67.

CHAMPION R. A., RUTTER S. M., PENNING P. D. AND ROOK A. J. (1994) Temporal variation in grazing behaviour of sheep and the reliability of sampling periods. *Applied Animal Behaviour Science),* **42**, 99-108.

COCHRAN W. G. AND COX G. M. (1964) *Experimental Design* (2nd edition), New York: Wiley. 611pp.

GOLDSTEIN H. (1995) Multilevel Statistical Models, 2nd Edition. *Kendall's Library of Statistics 3.* Arnold, London.

IASON G.R. AND ELSTON D.A. (2002) Groups, individuals, efficiency and validity of statistical analyses. *Applied Animal Behaviour Science,* **75**, 261-265.

KENWARD M. G. (1987) A method for comparing profiles of repeated measures. *Applied Statistics,* **36**, 296-308.

KNOWLES T.G. AND GREEN L.E. (2002) Multilevel statistical models allow simultaneous consideration of both individual and group effects. *Applied Animal Behaviour Science,* **77**, 335-336.

METZ J. H. AND MEKKING P. (1978) Adaptation in the feeding pattern of cattle according to social environment. *Proceedings of the Zodiac Symposium on Adaptation, Wageningen.* Wageningen, Centre for Agricultural Publishing and Documentation.

NEWMAN J. A., PENNING P. D., PARSONS A. J., HARVEY A. AND ORR, R. J. (1994). Fasting affects intake behaviour and diet preferences of grazing sheep. *Animal Behaviour,* **47**, 185-193.

PEARCE S. C. (1983) *The Agricultural Field Experiment: A Statistical Examination of Theory and Practice,* New York: Wiley. 335pp.

PEARCE S. C., CLARKE G. M., DYKE G. V. AND KEMPSON R. E. (1988) *A Manual of Crop Experimentation.* London: Charles Griffin. 358pp.

PENNING P. D., PARSONS A. J., NEWMAN J. A., ORR R. J. AND HARVEY A. (1993). The effects of group size on grazing time in sheep. *Applied Animal Behaviour Science,* **37**, 101-109.

PHILLIPS C.J.C. (1998) The use of individual animals as replicates in statistical analysis of their behaviour at pasture. *Applied Animal Behaviour Science,* **60**, 365-369.

PHILLIPS C.J.C. (2002) Further aspects of the use of individual animals as replicates in statistical analysis. *Applied Animal Behaviour Science,* **75**, 265-268.

PHILLIPS C. J. C. AND DENNE S. K. P. J. (1988) Variation in the grazing behaviour of dairy cows measured by a vibracorder and bite count monitor. *Applied Animal Behaviour Science,* **21**, 329-335.

RIND M.I. AND PHILLIPS C.J. (1999) The effect of group size on the ingestive and social behaviour of grazing dairy cows. *Animal Science,* **68**, 589-596.

ROOK A.J. (1999) The use of groups or individuals in the design of grazing experiments (reply to Phillips,1998). *Applied Animal Behaviour Science,* **61**, 357-358.

ROOK A. J. AND HUCKLE C. A. (1995) Synchronization of ingestive behaviour by grazing dairy cows. *Animal Science,* **60**, 25-30.

ROOK A. J., HUCKLE C. A. AND WILKINS R. J. (1994) The effects of sward height and concentrate supplementation on the performance of spring calving dairy cows grazing perennial ryegrass - white clover swards. *Animal Production,* **58**, 167-172.

ROOK A. J. AND PENNING P. D. (1991). Synchronisation of eating ruminating and idling activity by grazing sheep. *Applied Animal Behaviour Science*, **32**, 157-166.

ROOK A. J. AND PENNING P. D. (1991). Stochastic models of grazing behaviour in sheep. *Applied Animal Behaviour Science*, **32**, 167-177.

ROWELL J. G. AND WALTERS R. E. (1976) Analysing data with repeated observations on each experimental unit. *Journal of Agricultural Science, Cambridge*, **87**, 423-432.

SIEGEL S. AND CASTELLAN N. J. (1988) *Non-parametric Statistics for the Behavioural Sciences*. (2nd edition), New York: McGraw-Hill. 399pp.

SMITH H. K. AND HODGSON J. (1984) A note on the effect of recording frequency on the estimation of grazing time of cattle and sheep. *Applied Animal Ethology*, **11**, 229-236.

THOMAS H. AND LAIDLAW A. S. (1993) Planning, design, analysis and establishment of experiments: In: Davies, A., Baker, R. D., Grant, S. A. and Laidlaw, A. S. (eds.) *Sward Measurement Handbook* (2nd edition), pp. 13-37, Reading: British Grassland Society.

WEARY D.M. AND FRASER D. (1998) Replication and pseudo replication: a comment on Phillips (1998). *Applied Animal Behaviour Science*, **61**, 181-183.

# INDEX

## A

Accelerometer, 167, 169, 170
Accumulation factor, 28, 29
Accumulation rate, 31
Acid detergent fibre, 54, 62
Activity
    allowance, 97 99, 107
    increments, 98, 99
    pattern, 153, 154, 158, 161, 177, 178,
      182
Alkanes
    *see* N-alkane technique
Analogue
    format, 167, 169
    recording, 134, 166
    signal, 165
Animal production
    level, 96, 101,102
    measurement of, 104-105
Appetite, 131, 138
Artificial sward boards, 138-140
Associative effects, 71, 111
Automatic
    data analysis, 159, 164-166, 169
    data downloading, 168
    equipment, 154-170
    recording, 16, 74, 75, 151, 155, 156,
      158, 163, 164-170,
    systems, 156, 158
Autoscythes, 25

## B

Balance trial, 127
Behaviour patterns, 153, 158, 159
Bias, 15-18, 23, 25, 29, 32, 39, 42, 45,
    47-48, 58-59, 65, 68, 70, 83, 96,
    105, 111, 140, 158
Binoculars, 158, 161
Bite
    area, 138
    depth, 138

discrimination, 134, 139, 161, 166,
    168, 169
mass, 75, 76, 134, 135, 139, 151-
    152, 154-157, 162, 163, 169
number, 139, 155-157, 161, 162
Biting
    activity, 163, 164
    rate, 135, 136, 151-152, 154, 157,
      161
Body composition, 105
Botanical composition, 30, 40, 47, 48-
    50, 59, 66-67

## C

Cages, 32, 37-39, 43-45
Capacitance, 29-30
Cellulase technique, 65
Cellulose
    digestible, 71
    indigestible, 60, 71
    powder, 78, 80, 81
Changeover designs, 19
Chemical
    analysis, 24, 47, 55, 56, 58, 59, 63,
      67, 70, 81-82, 103
    composition, 103, 129
Chopping of herbage, 64, 122-124, 126,
    128, 129, 142
Chromic oxide
    accuracy of technique, 59
    carriers, 57
    dosing and sampling, 57-58
    errors and bias, 58
    estimation of faecal output, 56
    recovery rate, 58-59
Chromogen, 60
Collection
    of faeces, 54-56, 59, 62, 63
    of grazed samples, 66-70
    of samples by fistula, 68-70, 157,
      158
    of samples manually, 67